Gaëtan Rey · Jean-Yves Tigli ·
Erwin Franquet
Editors

Internet of Things

7th IFIPIoT 2024 International IFIP WG 5.5 Workshops

GRAAL4IoT 2024, STAND4IoT 2024
Posters, Nice, France, November 6–8, 2024
Proceedings

Springer

Editors
Gaëtan Rey (ID)
Université Côte d'Azur, CNRS, I3S, France
Sophia Antipolis, France

Jean-Yves Tigli (ID)
Université Côte d'Azur, CNRS, I3S, France
Sophia Antipolis, France

Erwin Franquet (ID)
Université Côte d'Azur, Polytech'Lab, France
Sophia Antipolis, France

ISSN 1868-4238   ISSN 1868-422X   (electronic)
IFIP Advances in Information and Communication Technology
ISBN 978-3-031-82064-9   ISBN 978-3-031-82065-6   (eBook)
https://doi.org/10.1007/978-3-031-82065-6

This Springer imprint is published by the registered company Springer Nature Switzerland AG
The registered company address is: Gewerbestrasse 11, 6330 Cham, Switzerland

If disposing of this product, please recycle the paper.

IFIP Advances in Information and Communication Technology

738

Editor-in-Chief

Kai Rannenberg, Goethe University Frankfurt, Germany

Editorial Board Members

IFIP Advances in Information and Communication Technology

The IFIP AICT series publishes state-of-the-art results in the sciences and technologies of information and communication. The scope of the series includes: foundations of computer science; software theory and practice; education; computer applications in technology; communication systems; systems modeling and optimization; information systems; ICT and society; computer systems technology; security and protection in information processing systems; artificial intelligence; and human-computer interaction.

Edited volumes and proceedings of refereed international conferences in computer science and interdisciplinary fields are featured. These results often precede journal publication and represent the most current research.

The principal aim of the IFIP AICT series is to encourage education and the dissemination and exchange of information about all aspects of computing.

More information about this series at https://link.springer.com/bookseries/6102

Preface

The rapid evolution of technology has led to the development of the Internet of Things (IoT), a network of physical objects that are embedded with sensors, software, and network connectivity, enabling them to collect and exchange data. The IoT is transforming our digital landscape, and the IFIP Internet of Things (IFIP-IoT) 2024 conference was a crucial platform for scholars, researchers, and practitioners to come together, share ideas, and advance this transformative field.

This edited book is a compilation of cutting-edge research and developments presented at the IFIP-IoT conference. The conference serves as a dynamic hub where experts from diverse backgrounds come together to explore the multifaceted aspects of IoT, from its technological foundations to its far-reaching implications for society, industry, and beyond.

The chapters in this book are a testament to the collaborative spirit of the IFIP-IoT community. They offer insights into the latest innovations, challenges, and opportunities in IoT, covering a wide array of topics, including IoT architectures, security and privacy, data analytics, edge computing, and applications in various domains. These contributions not only reflect the state of the art in IoT research but also provide valuable perspectives that pave the way for future breakthroughs.

The IFIP-IoT Conference is an annual IFIP event dedicated to IoT research, innovation, and applications, emphasizing the multidisciplinary nature of IoT. IoT encompasses topics from network protocols and embedded systems to analytics, machine learning, and social, legal, ethical, and economic considerations, enabling services in e-health, mobility, energy, manufacturing, smart cities, agriculture, and more. Security, privacy, and societal aspects are essential in IoT deployment. IFIP-IoT covers these diverse areas, seeking papers showcasing technical advancements, research, innovation, pilot results, and policy discussions. Contributors include researchers, users, organizations, ICT industry experts, authorities, and regulators.

IFIP-IoT 2024 welcomed full and short paper submissions, with full papers being original and unpublished elsewhere. The conference program featured keynotes, plenary talks, tutorials, technical sessions, special sessions, and expert panels. Two new workshops were added to the conference this year: STAND4IoT on various aspects of IoT standards and GRAAL4IoT on design, verification, and validation of IoT systems. A session was dedicated to the presentation of several Horizon Europe projects all contributing to IoT system security, design, and management. This session was initiated and organized by the DYNABIC EU project.

The conference, including the workshops, received a total of 33 submissions. 13 full papers and 4 short papers were accepted out of 28 submissions for the main conference. In addition 5 workshop papers and 3 poster papers were accepted for publication. The paper submission guidelines included an 18-page limit for full papers, which applied to both regular and workshop sessions, as well as a 12-page limit for short papers, applicable to any session. To ensure a thorough review process, we implemented a two-tier review mechanism within EasyChair, consisting of TPC Chairs, and TPC members as reviewers. Reviews were single-blind, with each submission receiving at least three reviews. We took measures to address conflicts of interest by appointing multiple TPC Chairs and multiple Track Chairs for each track. Additionally, we imposed a limit of 2 papers maximum for PC members. Furthermore, our conference included Regular Tracks/Sessions that accepted submissions from any authors, as well as Special Sessions/Tracks proposed by established researchers, with submissions received by invitation.

The IFIP-IoT conference had six regular tracks, each focusing on a different aspect of IoT:

- **Hardware/Software Solutions for IoT and CPS**: This track focused on the integration of hardware and software technologies to enable the development of efficient and scalable systems for the IoT and CPS. This track explored topics such as system architecture, energy-efficient hardware design, low-power communication protocols, software optimization for resource-constrained devices, and security and privacy issues. Additionally, this track highlighted recent advancements and future research directions in the field of IoT and CPS, including machine learning and artificial intelligence techniques, edge computing, and cloud-based systems.
- **Electronics and Signal Processing for IoT**: This track focused on the design and development of electronic devices and signal processing techniques for IoT applications. This track covered a broad range of topics, including sensor design, low-power electronics, wireless communication, and embedded systems. The track also explored signal processing techniques such as signal acquisition, filtering, compression, and analysis.
- **Networking and Communications Technology for IoT**: This track focused on the latest advancements and innovations in the field of IoT, in particular on IoT networking, wireless and wired communication technologies, protocols, standards, and applications.
- **Artificial Intelligence and Machine Learning Technologies for IoT**: This track focused on the integration of AI and ML techniques for IoT applications. This track covered a broad range of topics including the development of intelligent algorithms, big data analytics, and decision-making frameworks for IoT systems. The track also explored the use of AI and ML for predictive maintenance, anomaly detection, and optimization of IoT systems. The AI and ML track highlighted advancements and challenges in the field of IoT systems and their integration with AI and ML techniques.
- **Cyber Security/Privacy/Trust for IoT and CPS**: This track focused on the security and privacy challenges of IoT and CPS systems. This track covered a broad range of topics including cyber threats, privacy breaches, data breaches, and unauthorized access to IoT and CPS systems. The track also explored solutions for securing IoT and CPS systems, including cryptographic techniques, security protocols, intrusion detection, and prevention mechanisms. Additionally, this track discussed the challenges of maintaining trust and privacy in IoT and CPS systems and the importance of ethical considerations.

- **IoT or CPS Applications and Use Cases**: This track focused on exploring the real-world applications and use cases of IoT and CPS technology. The track brought together experts and professionals from various industries to discuss the challenges, opportunities, and innovative solutions for utilizing IoT and CPS to improve various domains such as healthcare, transportation, energy, agriculture, and others.

In addition to the session papers, the IFIP-IoT 2024 conference featured 2 workshops, 2 poster sessions, and 3 invited presentations. We are pleased to announce that all of these sessions took place and contributed to the IFIP-IoT 2024 conference:

- **GRAAL4IoT Workshop**: The GRAAL4IoT International Workshop was one of the most appropriate venues to discuss and advance all topics related to the design, verification, and validation of IoT systems, with a special focus on security. The main goals of the workshop were: (1) to encourage work on novel topics covering both fundamental and applied research in the design, verification, and validation of IoT systems, (2) to bring together researchers from the software development and IoT communities, and to foster discussions between theorists and practitioners.
- **STAND4IoT Workshop**: The international workshop Standards4IoT was the place to discuss all topics related to the standardization of IoT systems with different focuses. More specifically, the objectives of Standards4IoT were: (1) to gain a better understanding of the field of standardization and to demonstrate the concrete actions of this work; (2) to promote work on novel topics covering standardization research and/or education; (3) to bring together the IoT communities of industry, developers, and researchers to foster discussions on current common issues such as security, efficiency, and sustainability.
- **Invited Talks:**

  - **AI Detects and Mitigates Cyber-Attacks by Erol Gelenbe**: Simple cyber-attacks can disrupt networks for hours or days, compromise data security and cause unpredictable effects through malware. This underscores the importance of early detection and effective response. The presentation focused on the use of the Random Neural Network for cyber-attack detection, describing the mathematical model, deep learning algorithms, and concrete examples with low false alarm rates. Experiments with active mitigation strategies were also presented.
  - **Privacy in the IoT: Evolution and Expectations by Maryline Laurent**: Faced with the need to track the activity of objects, manage them flexibly and securely, detect anomalies, and make the best possible economic use of the data collected, it is imperative to preserve privacy in the IoT environment. The presentation identified the scientific challenges of IoT privacy with categories of solutions and then identified several emerging research topics in support of privacy preservation in the IOT.
  - **DEVS as a language for IoT System Design by Bernard P. Zeigler**: As IoT applications evolve, adaptive behaviours become essential. Although complex adaptive systems have existed in theory for some time, their implementation in operational IoT systems is still evolving. The DEVS formalism enables modular,

adaptive modelling, facilitating verification and the transition between design and implementation of IoT systems.

We are grateful to the authors who contributed their expertise to these volumes, and we commend their dedication to advancing the field of IoT. We would also like to acknowledge the reviewers whose insightful feedback ensured the quality and rigor of the included chapters.

We hope that these edited books will serve as a valuable resource for researchers, educators, policymakers, and industry professionals alike, fostering a deeper under- standing of IoT and inspiring further innovation in this transformative domain. As the IFIP-IoT conference continues to evolve and grow, we look forward to witnessing the continued impact of this vibrant community on the ever-expanding Internet of Things.

November 2024

Gaëtan Rey
Jean-Yves Tigli
Erwin Franquet

Organization

General Chairs

Gaëtan Rey	Université Côte d'Azur, France
Jean-Yves Tigli	Université Côte d'Azur, France
Erwin Franquet	Université Côte d'Azur, France

Technical Program Chairs

Ana Rosa Cavalli	Institut Polytechnique de Paris, France
Bidyadhar Subudhi	Indian Institute of Technology Goa, India
Lei Chen	Georgia Southern University, USA
Leonardo Lizzi	University of Trento, Italy
Phu Nguyen	SINTEF, Norway
Srinivas Katkoori	University of South Florida, USA
Te-Chuan Chiu	National Tsing Hua University, Taiwan

Workshops Chairs

Nicolas Ferry	Université Côte d'Azur, France
Marie-Agnès Peraldi-Frati	Université Côte d'Azur, France

Technical Program Committee

Mike Borowczak	University of Central Florida, USA
Karima Boudaoud	Université Côte d'Azur, France
Laurent Capocchi	Université de Corse, France
Sibi Chakkaravarthy S.	VIT-AP University, India
Lei Chen	Georgia Southern University, USA
Te-Chuan Chiu	National Tsing Hua University, Taiwan
Jiban Das	Georgia Southern University, USA
Kaustubh Dhondge	Glaukes Labs, USA
Fabien Ferrero	Université Côte d'Azur, France
Nicolas Ferry	Université Côte d'Azur, France
Erwin Franquet	Université Côte d'Azur, France
Agbotiname Imoize	University of Lagos, Nigeria
Dheryta Jaisinghani	University of Northern Iowa, USA
Jongyeop Kim	Georgia Southern University, USA
Ashok Kumar	IBM, USA
Stéphane Lavirotte	Université Côte d'Azur, France
Leonardo Lizzi	University of Trento, Italy
Dino Lopez	Université Côte d'Azur, France

Veena Mendiratta	Northwestern University, USA
Atef Mohamed	Georgia Southern University, USA
Luong Nguyen	Montimage, France
Manhdung Nguyen	Montimage, France
Phu Nguyen	SINTEF, Norway
Tasnim Onisha	Georgia Southern University, USA
Peetabasa Pati	Amrita University Bangalore, India
Marie-Agnès Peraldi-Frati	Université Côte d'Azur, France
Gaëtan Rey	Université Côte d'Azur, France
Gérald Rocher	Université Côte d'Azur, France
Sriram Sankaran	Amrita University, India
Sharma Sharad	University of North Texas, USA
Pradip Sharma	University of Aberdeen, UK
Leon Strous	IFIP, The Netherlands
Jean-Yves Tigli	Université Côte d'Azur, France
Weitian Tong	Georgia Southern University, USA
Sergi Trilles Oliver	UJI, Spain
Meenalosini Vimal Cruz	Georgia Southern University, USA
Antonio Virdis	Università di Pisa, Italy
Kai Wang	Georgia Southern University, USA
Hao Zhang	Georgia Southern University, USA

Web Chair

Gaëtan Rey	Université Côte d'Azur, France

Contents

STAND4IoT'24: First International Workshop on IoT Standards

IFIP IoT'24 Posters Session

An Open Source Trusted Edge Architecture of Federated Dataspaces for the Food Supply Chain

Alexander Tessmer[1]([⊠]), Jannis Mast[1]([⊠]), Philipp Loer[2], Matthias Brunner[3],
Felix Lippert[2], and Nils Aschenbruck[1]([⊠])

[1] Osnabrueck University, Institute of Computer Science, Osnabrueck, Germany
`{tessmer,jmast,aschenbruck}@uos.de`
[2] Lippert Inspection GmbH, Sinzig am Rhein, Germany
`{philipp.loer,felix.lippert}@lippert-qm.com`
[3] tsenso GmbH, Stuttgart, Germany
`m.brunner@tsenso.com`

Abstract. Currently, quality assurance in the food supply chain is predominantly conducted manually with traditional destructive methods. Best before date forecasts depend mainly on time of arrival without including weather or cold chain. Measured data within the food supply chain is not digitized and can therefore not be aggregated for analysis.

We propose a new architecture for improving sustainability of the food supply by combining innovative measurement techniques with a trusted cloud edge infrastructure. Forecasts based on digital twins and a shared federated data space for freshness data serve to optimize supply chain processes and reduce the loss of fresh produce along the supply chain. In this paper, we present a suitable system architecture with independent data spaces and flexible implementations for trusted local deployments.

Keywords: Trusted Edge · Food Supply Chain · Federated Dataspaces

1 Introduction

Traditional methods of food quality assurance based on visual, chemical, or biological inspection are destructive, time-consuming, and sometimes harmful to the environment. Modern visual and spectral measurement methods, like a scanner or hyperspectral camera, are capable of capturing a large amount of relevant data for food quality assurance with non-destructive methods. Specifically in the context of agriculture, various plant parameters for health, ripeness and more can be identified and evaluated.

Currently, mostly traditional methods are used for food quality assurance and various levels of digitization are present. Manual paper logs, spreadsheets, and smartphone application based questionnaires are methods used. Even though

© IFIP International Federation for Information Processing 2025
Published by Springer Nature Switzerland AG 2025
G. Rey et al. (Eds.): IFIPIoT 2024, IFIP AICT 738, pp. 3–11, 2025.
https://doi.org/10.1007/978-3-031-82065-6_1

all data is typically stored in proprietary databases, the value of this data is unused along the supply chain. Food waste is still present in later stages of the supply chain. A flexible system for incorporating this proprietary data is needed to enable data share and provide value by using this information to sort out food in the earlier supply chain stages, where it may be used elsewhere.

Our overarching goal is to improve the sustainability of food supply by reducing food waste in the supply chain. We believe that this goal can be reached by providing trusted information that can be used for making informed decisions earlier in the food supply chain through shared event data of digital twins along the supply chain. This paper focuses on providing a trusted system architecture as a foundation concept for the sharing of data between enterprise data spaces. The main contributions of our system architecture are: (1) A use case driven design with requirement analysis, (2) the incorporation of separate autonomous data spaces, which enable the realization of confidentiality requirements, (3) a security and privacy by design architecture, and (4) the incorporation of a prevalent linked data schema to enable data sharing between non-interoperable technologies.

2   Background and Related Approaches

There are many trusted edge-based Internet of Things (IoT) architectures. [4] surveys and summarizes the state-of-the-art and research challenges. [1] surveys data collection and management along the food supply chain using blockchain technology. This provides a baseline for trusted edge-based system architectures. Our approach is a flexible trusted system architecture that can incorporate these solutions and provides the overarching trusted concept to connect different systems in the context of the food supply chain. To the best of our knowledge, a trusted edge architecture for the food supply chain has not been developed before.

FIWARE [2] is an open source platform for developing smart solutions with digital twins and data spaces. It provides many parts needed for a system deployment, e.g., a large database of data models and multiple implementations of IoT architectures like context manager systems. They focus on single data space concepts. In our new architecture, we propose a use of the newest systems that support linked data used in a trusted web context to provide local context data for incorporating in the event based supply chain.

Electronic Product Code Information Services (EPCIS) [6] is a global GS1 standard for creating and sharing event data between enterprises and enables users to link physical or digital objects to relevant enterprise data. It is already heavily used in the logistics sector. Additionally, EPCIS can be easily extended with new data types and support exporting data into other formats, e.g., the in a web context widespread JSON format.

Gaia-X [5] is a federated secure data infrastructure based on blockchain transactions to provide a basis to exchange data across multiple actors. It aims to let users retain autonomy and self-determination with their non-interoperable technologies by sharing data through trusted platforms that comply with common rules.

3 Requirement Analysis

The implementation of a trusted edge architecture in the food supply chain, particularly the quality inspection of fresh fruits and vegetables, requires careful consideration of specific requirements. The data obtained helps to objectively assess the current (and future) quality status of the perishable products.

The **accuracy** of the data is of crucial importance, as economic transactions depend on it. Given the perishability of the products and the often short shelf life, the trade in fruits and vegetables is a time-critical sector. Therefore, rapid **availability** of measurement results is essential. The trusted edge architecture must be able to process data almost in real time and provide immediate feedback so that a decision can be made about further action with the inspected goods and to avoid food waste in the supply chain due to slow processes. The measurements and results must be **reliable** in order to make informed decisions. This requires high accuracy and consistency of the measurements. Furthermore, the architecture must be flexible for a **heterogeneous** hardware setup by being able to be composed of various devices, including mobile phones, tablets, PCs, and other components. However, the scanners that perform the measurement and bring the data into the trusted edge environment must be **lightweight** and mobile for use in the warehouse. Competition for fruit and vegetables is very tough and is based on the company's own specifications (quality attributes). These must be protected from unauthorized access, as must be data on the origin of the products. Thus, the **security** of the captured data is an important aspect. Therefore, the system must implement robust security measures to ensure data integrity. **Horizontal scalability** is required to allow the architecture to be deployed in multiple different locations. Furthermore, **vertical scaling** enables the system to dynamically adapt to changing amounts of measurements that need to be processed in a given time frame, allowing the architecture to efficiently support varying workloads at each location.

These specific requirements ensure that the trusted edge architecture can be effectively used in the quality inspections of fresh fruits and vegetables. It enables accurate quality assessment, rapid result availability, high data security, and reliable measurements, while simultaneously offering a flexible hardware architecture. Using such systems in combination with non-destructive measurements will speed up the inspection process, which itself will help to enhance the sample size and volume of gained data. These aspects together contribute to ensuring the quality and safety in the food supply chain.

4 System Architecture

For the adoption of a new trusted edge system in the food supply chain, the system design has to maximize acceptance by providing value in logging or analysis as well as being compatible to existing approaches. Therefore, the system architecture is designed to incorporate existing data spaces into a federated set. The concept for the system architecture, as displayed in Fig. 1 is separated into three layers:

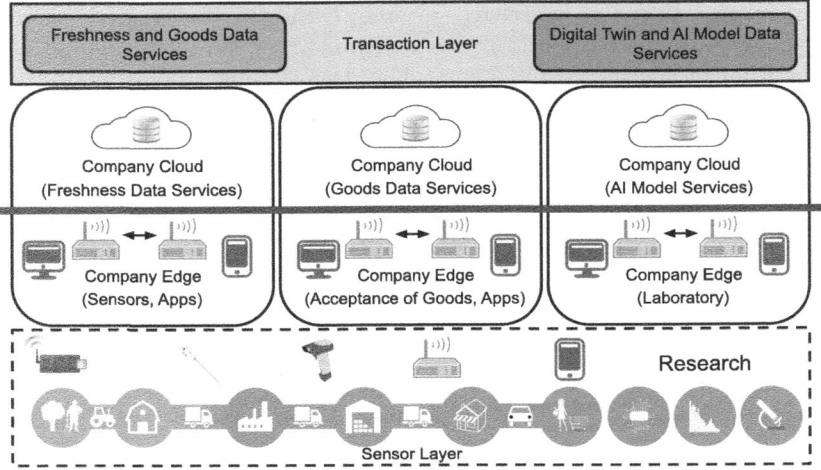

Fig. 1. Concept of architecture

- The **Sensor Layer** incorporates all sensors and devices, which do not actively participate in the system. On one hand, this includes all sensors with or without their own measurement device and their own data interface. On the other hand, user terminals and workstations can be considered as sensors of user interaction and are therefore also included. These system peripheral sensors are conceptually separated into the bottom system layer, because they can be interacted with from any Core Layer point, e.g. weather stations could be accesses by multiple data spaces as well as at the edge or by a cloud service. Also, user terminals may be directly connected to the cloud for maintainers or locally at a test site.
- The **Core Layer** is defined by the set of all separated data spaces, which could be considered the community of the enterprises that participate. All devices in this layer differ from a Sensor Layer device by implementing a minimum set of the system interface. They provide services that include the interfaces for system interaction and management.
  - The **Cloud** is the core of the data space and is often already present in an enterprise. It acts as a data storage and serves as an interface to the Transaction Layer, where services can be supplied.
  - The **Edge** is a subordinate part of the data space. It describes a set of locally deployed networks that keep location specific redundant context

data to enable robust services even without secured internet connection. Therefore, the Edge in a data space can exist as multiple deployed networks or not at all.

– The top level **Transaction Layer** defines the interface between the data spaces of the Core Layer. It consists of a shared database of linked metadata in a hierarchical structure that provides the blueprint for data communication between data spaces. Lower levels of the data structure may be present in a private data space and the link only resolves for authorized agents. The authentication system of the private enterprise data space has to enable access to the data structure metadata for all agents with access to the described data.

4.1 System Deployment

The concept for the system architecture creates a flexible communication infrastructure. Requirements for the trusted system architecture are the security core components confidentiality, integrity, and availability. At least all outgoing communication is encrypted and within a data space, confidentiality and integrity can be provided by any system, chosen by the data space owner.

For the data spaces, the overarching interface is described by the transaction layer. We propose the W3C Schema [12] for metadata structure descriptions of the services as it is already prevalent. Multiple implementations can be chosen for federated data sharing. For example, either Electronic Product Code Information Services (EPCIS) as an already established data share for logistics or Gaia-X, an upcoming blockchain-based federated framework, are possible. Communication to the system is secured and the trust-level is provided and dependent on the system used.

The Cloud in the Core Layer has to be extended to provide the data structure of its services as metadata. Only chosen services are published to the Transaction Layer and providing service data structure improves data sharing. Additional metadata can improve trust into the data itself. Additionally, no actual data, even structural data, has to be public. A link can be published while all related data is secured within the private data space.

The Edge deployment is separated into distinct local networks. A constant connection to the Cloud is not assured. An Edge deployment can be anything between a locally running smartphone application or a fully distributed edge network. Each deployment should have a central node that manages context data and its position in the hierarchical data structure. It can provide redundant service data to facilitate local availability of Cloud services. In a fully distributed case this can include a replicated database as well as a load balancer and service migration for local services.

5 Prototypic Realization

We demonstrate our architecture in the form of an initial prototype system that implements the classification of tomatoes as an example of an application during the supply chain. Incoming shipments of tomatoes are to be evaluated by

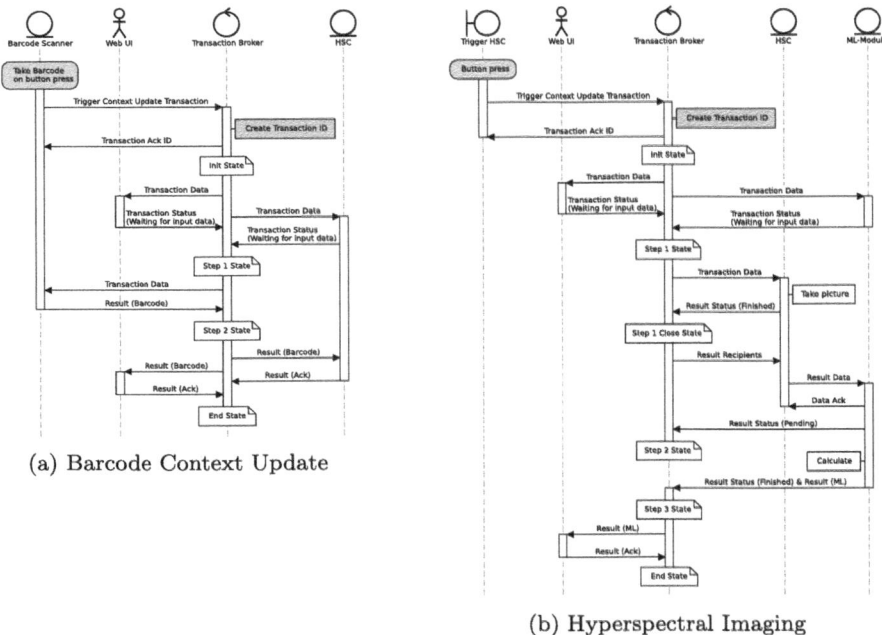

(a) Barcode Context Update

(b) Hyperspectral Imaging

Fig. 2. Communication sequences of hyperspectral imaging evaluation example

hyperspectral imaging. First an operator scans the barcode label. After positioning a crate underneath the hyperspectral camera, the operator triggers the camera through a button. These pictures are then processed by a machine learning model alongside temperature measurements collected by sensors inside the tomato crates during transport. The result is a classification of the tomatoes' current condition that is shown within the system's web interface so the operator can use the information to make decisions about what to do with the shipment.

We implement the prototype as a set of distributed software containers using Docker [9], an established open-source platform for container deployment and management. Packaging individual system components within containers allows them to be deployed on any machine within our system regardless of its architecture and installed software components. It also enables easy future inclusion of components supplied by third parties such as externally developed machine learning models that may have their own prerequisites which can be included inside the respective container.

For management and coordination, we deploy the FIWARE Orion-LD Context Broker [3]. Orion-LD implements the NGSI-LD specification [7], an extended subset of JSON-LD, a format for storing and transmitting linked data. Through this implementation, importing data using the Resource Description Framework (RDF) [11] is also possible. The broker is responsible for keeping track of all deployed services, their locations, interfaces and the associated data schema for each interface. MongoDB [10] is used as the database backend for Orion-LD, providing persistent storage of context data.

Additional containers provide interfaces for the camera and temperature sensors. The machine learning model is deployed on an NVIDIA Jetson Nano, which provides hardware-accelerated machine learning capabilities. This showcases the prototype's ability to deploy components on different hardware depending on each component's requirements enabled by our distributed and modular architecture. Finally, we include a container running a web server which can be accessed from a computer or smartphone to trigger measurements and view the results. The web interface uses WebAuthn [8] to authenticate users through FIDO2-compatible hardware tokens in order to ensure that only authorized and trusted users can access the system and enter data.

Figure 2 shows specific communication sequences of a hyperspectral image evaluation. Each communication follows a RESTful query response pattern, although the query target entity is not strictly also the response entity. Every data packet is linked to a data flow instance, also called Transaction, and the Transaction State is tracked by the Transaction Broker. The context establishment is facilitated by the system setup, context data from the transaction layer, as well as scanning the barcode of a shipment crate. Note that while data flow targets and transactions are managed by the Transaction Broker, the large image data is only transmitted directly between the relevant entities.

6 Evaluation

We evaluate our prototype based on the requirements described in Sect. 3. Our architecture can ensure **accuracy** of the results by assigning a trust level to acquired data such as sensor readings and machine learning results, which is transmitted and stored alongside the values as linked data and aggregated during data processing to create forwarded trust information. **Availability** is achieved through caching external data sources locally and providing an upload queue for results, eliminating the requirement of a permanently available internet connection. The architecture is **reliable**, because service containers can be seamlessly migrated between hosts in case of a hardware failure. This ability also provides **flexibility** as services can be dynamically migrated to different devices to meet the deployment's individual requirements. In combination with the device-agnostic RESTful interfaces, container migration allows for **heterogeneity**, as device-specific implementations of a service can be replaced with alternatives during migration without requiring any special handling within other system components. Containerization of individual services additionally enables **lightweightness**, because the container's low overhead allows individual services to be deployed on low-power nodes, where the requirement is present. Because our architecture is designed as a standalone cluster of services, **horizontal scalability** is guaranteed since separate deployments can be set up without the need of interconnecting services between different deployments. The concept of using a coordinating scheduler realizes **vertical scalability** as the scheduler can implement load balancing across multiple instances of the same service. Transmitting data through direct connections between service containers rather than through the scheduler prevents it from becoming a bottleneck when scaling up. Finally, the architecture maintains **security** by containing data within its own separated data space, while using HTTPS as a well-established protocol that provides state-of-the-art encryption and authentication for communication between services over a potentially untrusted network.

7   Conclusion

In this paper, a trusted-edge IoT system and communication architecture was presented, enabling sharing of data between separated data spaces of the food supply chain with a federated design. We investigated specific design challenges in the food supply chain and evaluated our architecture regarding these requirements. With the design of separate data spaces with a multitude of individual deployment choices, we exemplarily deployed a distributed edge prototype as a proof-of-concept. In our future work, we will successively extend and iterate over our example deployment by integrating special sensors, e.g., hyperspectral camera, and improving upon the user interface.

Acknowledgments. This research is part of the project FRED and was funded by the German Federal Ministry for Economic Affairs and Climate Action (BMWK) within the funding program "Entwicklung digitaler Technologien" with contract number 01MD22003A. We would like to thank Martin Atzmueller, Victor Chernikh, Arnab Ghosh Chowdhury and Steffen Meinert for their productive feedback. The authors are responsible for the contents of this publication.

References

1. Fiore, M., Mongiello, M.: Blockchain technology to support agri-food supply chains: a comprehensive review. IEEE Access **11**, 75311–75324 (2023). https://doi.org/10.1109/ACCESS.2023.3296849
2. FIWARE foundation: FIWARE (2024). https://www.fiware.org/
3. FIWARE foundation: Orion-LD. GitHub repository (2024). https://github.com/FIWARE/context.Orion-LD
4. Fotia, L., Delicato, F., Fortino, G.: Trust in edge-based internet of things architectures: State of the art and research challenges. ACM Comput. Surv. **55**(9) (2023). https://doi.org/10.1145/3558779
5. Gaia-X European association for data and cloud (AISBL): Gaia-X trust framework (2024). https://gaia-x.eu/
6. GS1: EPCIS & CBV (2022). https://www.gs1.org/standards/epcis
7. Industry Specification Group (ISG) cross-cutting context information management (CIM): context information management (CIM); NGSI-LD API. ETSI GS CIM 009 (2023). https://www.etsi.org/deliver/etsi_gs/CIM/001_099/009/01.07.01_60/gs_CIM009v010701p.pdf
8. Jones, M.B., Kumar, A., Lundberg, E.: Web authentication: an API for accessing public key credentials - level 3 (2023). https://www.w3.org/TR/webauthn-3/

9. Merkel, D.: Docker: lightweight Linux containers for consistent development and deployment. Linux J. **2014**(239), 2 (2014)
10. MongoDB, Inc.: MongoDB. https://www.mongodb.com/
11. RDFCore working group: resource description framework (RDF) (2004). https://www.w3.org/RDF/
12. W3C Schema.org community group: Schema.org (2024). https://schema.org/

Design and Experimentation
of a Distributed Information
Retrieval-Hybrid Architecture in Cloud
IoT Data Centers

Davide Tosi$^{(\boxtimes)}$ (iD) and Roberto Pazzi (iD)

Università dell'Insubria, Via Ravasi 2, Varese, Italy
{davide.tosi,roberto.pazzi}@uninsubria.it

Abstract. The proliferation of data from IoT devices has introduced challenges for efficient and accurate information retrieval in distributed Cloud Data Centers. This paper presents a Hybrid Distributed Information Retrieval (H-DIR) model optimized for IoT environments using advanced semantics and a hybrid query approach. The model aims to improve retrieval precision and efficiency by leveraging semantic concepts and contextual metadata, while also enhancing security and data privacy. Applied in a real industrial setting for gardening services, the H-DIR model demonstrates potential to increase revenue through economic quantification of services and value creation via faster preventive measures.

Keywords: Distributed Information Retrieval · Cloud IoT Data Centers · Heterogeneous Sensors · Interoperability · Security · Semantic

1 Introduction

Problem Background: The Internet of Things (IoT) enables a global network of interconnected devices, reducing the need for direct human-machine interaction, supported by various sensors and actuators [3]. However, the heterogeneous data generated by these sensors presents challenges in effective utilization due to its unstructured nature [23].

This paper investigates the use of semantic web technologies to enhance information retrieval from IoT sensors, addressing challenges of data heterogeneity and interoperability by mapping structured sensor data to unstructured formats [4]. We employ Big Data techniques like Spark and SPARK-SQL to boost interoperability, integrating them with SPARQL to create an advanced hybrid system [5,17].

The architecture leverages semantic techniques for modeling streaming sensor data within a Distributed Information Retrieval (DIR) context, resulting in a

---

D. Tosi and R. Pazzi—These authors contributed equally to this work.

G. Rey et al. (Eds.): IFIPIoT 2024, IFIP AICT 738, pp. 12–21, 2025.
https://doi.org/10.1007/978-3-031-82065-6_2

Hybrid DIR (H-DIR) architecture that enables distributed search in the cloud using Apache Jena [7]. This paper evaluates the H-DIR architecture through a smart gardening case study, where it integrates semantic web technologies with traditional IoT frameworks.

This paper evaluates the H-DIR architecture within a smart gardening case study, innovatively integrating semantic web technologies with traditional IoT frameworks. The remainder of the paper is organized as follows: Section 2 discusses related work, Sect. 3 describes the H-DIR architecture, Sect. 4 presents the gardening case study, and Sect. 5 concludes with a summary and discussion of results.

2   Related Work

This paper explores a Distributed Information Retrieval (DIR) model in cloud data centers, integrating Big Data and semantic web technologies to enhance IoT data retrieval for gardening services, addressing data heterogeneity and interoperability challenges.

Building on foundational works [12,21] that transformed IoT sensor data for smart farming, our study further leverages cloud-based systems to improve data processing and retrieval, extending the advancements made by [2,15]. Additionally, we build on optimization efforts in smart gardening [1,19] and enhance data interoperability using Semantic Sensor Service Networks [25], integrating Apache SPARK for better query performance [17].

Our research develops a more dynamic Hybrid Distributed Information Retrieval (H-DIR) model, significantly improving IoT data retrieval efficiency and scalability in cloud environments.

3   H-DIR Design: The Proposed Architecture

In this section, an advanced Distributed Information Retrieval-Hybrid (H-DIR) architecture is proposed and discussed.

3.1   H-DIR Employed Tools and Technologies

The H-DIR framework integrates Big Data, AI, and Natural Language Processing (NLP) with advanced preprocessing techniques to structure IoT sensor data for analysis. NLP is crucial in transforming unstructured data into formats suitable for semantic analysis, enhancing the framework's ability to manage data heterogeneity.

The architecture employs Description Logic (DL) for its analytical engine, enabling structured analysis of complex IoT data [26]. This tool generates new insights and rules from existing datasets, revealing patterns and relationships not initially apparent.

DL models are integrated into the SPARK framework, using Hadoop to manage large-scale data workloads [10]. Embedding SPARQL within this framework enhances query efficiency, combining Apache Spark SQL's processing capabilities with SPARQL's semantic functions for nuanced data analysis. A key innovation of the H-DIR architecture is its hybrid query methodology that adeptly handles both structured and unstructured data types. This method, vital for navigating the diverse data landscapes of IoT environments, marries Apache Spark SQL's processing capabilities with SPARQL's advanced semantic query functions, thereby facilitating nuanced, context-rich data analysis.

The framework also includes a version control and change management system based on ontological analysis, ensuring data integrity. By fusing neural networks (RNNs, LSTMs, GRUs, CNNs, Transformers) with OntoSensor and SensorML frameworks, the architecture supports complex queries and advanced analytics, enabling actionable insights from sensor data.

3.2   H-DIR Layers

The H-DIR architecture is divided into five layers, each handling different aspects of information retrieval. This structure simplifies complexity, enhances data analysis, and allows flexibility while improving security by compartmentalizing functions. Figure 1 illustrates these layers.

- **Layer 1 - NodeMCU-based Monitoring System**: This layer integrates a NodeMCU-based system with sensors and cameras for anomaly detection in real-time, focusing on optimizing placement, storage, bandwidth, and security [6,16].
- **Layer 2 - RDF Mapping and Sensor Data Integration**: This layer focuses on integrating and mapping sensor data into RDF using standardized web formats, enhancing semantic data analysis and decision-making through technologies like the Semantic Sensor Network Ontology, RDF, SPARQL, and IoT-Lite [8,22,27].
- **Layer 3 - Reasoning Modeled Ontology**: This layer uses Description Logic (DL), OWL, and SWRL for knowledge representation and reasoning [17]. Components include query processing, indexing, storage, and result aggregation [18]. Integration of OntoSensor ontology and SensorML [www.ogc.org/standard/sensorml] supports complex data representation in areas like environmental monitoring and agricultural management.
- **Layer 4 - Apache Spark Integration**: Combines Apache Spark with the D2RQ platform [d2rq.org] to access relational databases as RDF graphs, optimizing data processing in a semantically enriched ecosystem [11]. Spark's distributed processing enhances information retrieval, while D2RQ bridges relational databases and RDF data [9].
- **Layer 5 - Hybrid System H-DIR**: This layer integrates Apache Jena to manage RDF data, with a translation layer converting SPARQL queries into Spark SQL for seamless interaction between relational and semantic data. IoT sensor data is stored in HDFS for scalability, with Spark SQL optimizing structured data processing and SPARQL handling semantic queries. The key focus is on ensuring efficient interoperability between Spark and Jena, supporting effective data management and system scalability [20].

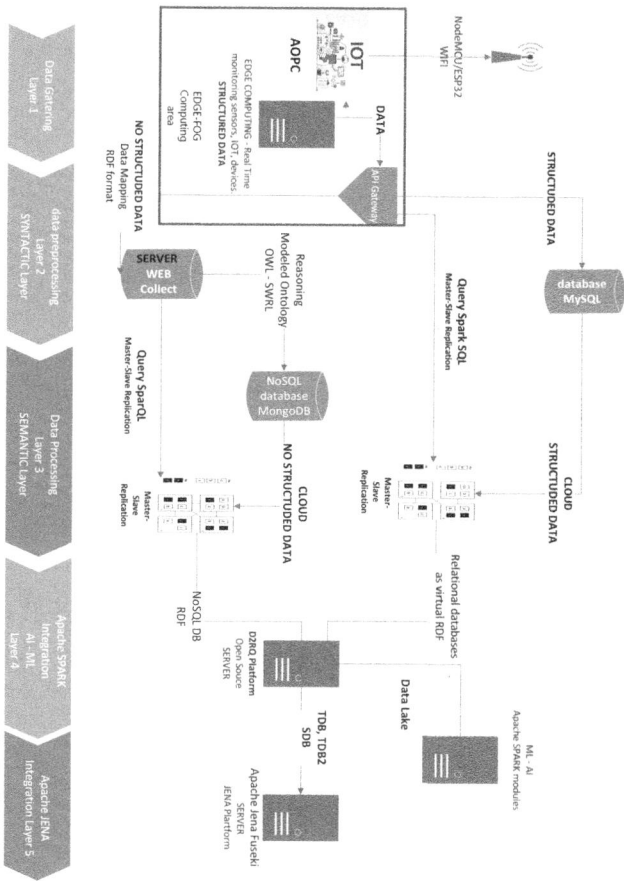

Fig. 1. H-DIR Architecture: structural layers and adopted technologies

4 H-DIR Experimentation Results: the Greenhouse Case Study

This section describes the experimentation of the H-DIR architecture in a real greenhouse for agricultural monitoring, detailing the customized H-DIR layers and concluding with a discussion of the results.

4.1 Customized H-DIR Architectural Layers: an Overview

Each layer of our designed H-DIR architecture has been customized to manage the specific agricultural monitoring case study. Specifically:

- **Layer1** provides real-time monitoring of agricultural conditions using sensors and cameras to collect data on temperature, humidity, light levels, and plant health, crucial for gathering raw data from the field.
- **Layer2** integrates and maps the collected data into RDF format, allowing for semantic interpretation and enrichment with metadata, leading to a comprehensive view of agricultural conditions.
- **Layer3** applies descriptive logic and ontologies to infer new information, such as potential plant risks or crop needs, based on the integrated data.
- **Layer4** utilizes Apache Spark for distributed computing, processing large data volumes, and enabling advanced analyses like crop condition predictions and water resource optimization.
- **Layer5** integrates all components, using Apache Jena to manage, query, and reason over RDF data, facilitating data interaction through SPARQL queries adapted to work with Spark SQL.

The theoretical layers are practically implemented in the agricultural monitoring experiment by tailoring each layer to address the specific needs of data collection, integration, analysis, and usage within the agricultural context.

4.2 Customized H-DIR Architectural Layers: Technical Details

Our H-DIR architecture was deployed in three greenhouses for monitoring Blueberry Ash plants (Fraxinus Quadrangulata), utilizing ten sensors and three cameras to collect environmental and plant health data in real-time, specifically within **Layer 2**. This includes temperature, humidity, light intensity, and plant height measurements to detect health variances.

In **Layer 3**, we integrate Long Short-Term Memory (LSTM) and Gated Recurrent Units (GRUs) [24] to process time series data, enabling predictive modeling of plant growth based on environmental trends. Implemented in Python, we used TensorFlow (version 2.14.0) and Keras libraries for model training [14].

Through NLP, **Layer 3** also analyzes both quantitative sensor data and textual data about Blueberry Ash plants Listing 1.1. After text preprocessing, texts are transformed into numerical vectors to capture semantic relationships (Line 6). A pre-trained Sentiment Analysis transformers model detects the tone of texts (Line 10), providing insights into general perceptions or opinions about the plants. Additionally, another transformer model is employed for question answering based on the processed text context (Line 15).

In **Layer 4**, semantically enriched and normalized sensor and camera data are integrated with other RDF-linked data and queried using SPARQL. This allows, for example, retrieving temperature readings from specific sensors and correlating them with RDF data representing weather conditions at the same location. Listing 1.2 illustrates a SPARQL query, defining the base URI prefix for domain-specific terms, specifying variables like plant identifiers, leaf measurements, and water quality metrics, and matching RDF data patterns to return structured results.The SELECT clause allows to specify the variables to be returned by the query, such as plants identified as '?plant', their leaf measurements ('?leafWidth', '?leafHeight'), and water quality metrics ('?waterQualityMetric'). The WHERE clause allows to define a pattern that RDF data must match for the specified variables in the SELECT clause to be returned.

The query looks for entities of type 'ash:BlueberryAsh' (Blueberry Ash plants), their leaf measurements ('ash:hasLeafMeasurement') which include width ('ash:width') and height ('ash:height'), and values related to water quality ('ash:hasWaterQuality' with metric 'ash:metric'). Finally, the results are ordered and organized in a more readable and structured manner.

Data normalization in **Layer 4** ensures homogeneous LSTM inputs, crucial for accurate modeling of environmental impacts on plant growth. The Adam optimizer and Mean Squared Error (MSE) loss function guide the training process [13].

```
# Preprocessing: Tokenization and removal of stopwords
stop_words = set(stopwords.words('english'))
preprocessed_texts = [ .join([word for word in nltk.
    word_tokenize(text.lower()) if word.isalnum() and not
    word in stop_words]) for text in data_texts]

# Word Embeddings with Word2Vec
model = Word2Vec([text.split() for text in
    preprocessed_texts], vector_size=100, window=5,
    min_count=1, workers=4)
word_vectors = model.wv

# Sentiment Analysis with Transformers
sentiment_pipeline = pipeline("sentiment-analysis")
sentiment_results = [sentiment_pipeline(text) for text in
    preprocessed_texts]
print("Sentiment Analysis Results:", sentiment_results)

# Question Answering with Transformers
question_answering_pipeline = pipeline("question-
    answering")
context = .join(preprocessed_texts)
question = "What do gardeners appreciate about Blueberry
    Ash?"
answer = question_answering_pipeline(question=question,
    context=context)
print(f"Answer: {answer['answer']}, Score: {answer['score
    ']}")

# Assuming 'water_quality' and 'soil_quality' are columns
    in the dataset
# Calculating the average water quality
average_water_quality = data['water_quality'].mean()
```

```
25  print(f"Average water quality during the Blueberry Ash
        growth period: {average_water_quality}/10")
26
27  # Calculating the average soil quality
28  average_soil_quality = data['soil_quality'].mean()
29  print(f"Average soil quality during the Blueberry Ash
        growth period: {average_soil_quality}/10")
```

Listing 1.1. Example Python Code for Data Processing and Analysis

```
1  PREFIX ash: <http://example.org/raspberryash#>
2  PREFIX xsd: <http://www.w3.org/2001/XMLSchema#>
3
4  SELECT ?plant ?leafWidth ?leafHeight ?waterQualityMetric
5  WHERE {
6    ?plant rdf:type ash:BlueberryAsh .
7    ?plant ash:hasLeafMeasurement ?leafMeasurement .
8    ?leafMeasurement ash:width ?leafWidth .
9    ?leafMeasurement ash:height ?leafHeight .
10   ?plant ash:hasWaterQuality ?waterQuality .
11   ?waterQuality ash:metric ?waterQualityMetric .
12 }
13 ORDER BY ?plant
```

Listing 1.2. SPARQL Query for Retrieving Plant Data

In **Layer 5**, correlating RDF-linked data enables comprehensive analysis of integrated data. For example, historical sensor data in RDF format can be analyzed to identify patterns or anomalies in environmental conditions. Integrating sensor data with RDF datasets, such as geographical information, supports location-based analysis and decision-making, enhancing our understanding of sensor data within a broader semantic web.

We conducted a correlation analysis between environmental factors and Blueberry Ash plant growth. By integrating sensor data with external datasets https://data.nsw.gov.au/, the analysis highlighted the significant impact of water and soil quality on plant growth, underscoring their importance in the H-DIR architecture.

4.3 Discussion

This study enhanced IoT data interoperability using semantic web and Big Data techniques within the H-DIR architecture, which streamlined data processing. However, ensuring scalability requires advanced hardware for real-time processing of diverse IoT sensor data. Specifically:

Horizontal Scaling: Support the addition of more worker nodes to increase computational capacity, enabling efficient handling of increasing data volumes.

Real-Time Processing: Utilize Apache Kafka for managing real-time data streams from sensors and cameras, ensuring timely data processing and analysis.

Monitoring and Optimization: Implement monitoring tools like Prometheus and Grafana to track system performance and optimize resource utilization dynamically.

Resource Optimization: Employ load balancing techniques to distribute workloads evenly across the nodes, maximizing the use of available resources.

Advanced hardware and efficient Big Data and semantic web technologies are vital for the scalability and performance of H-DIR architectures. Future efforts will focus on broadening applications and improving integration to enhance IoT systems and develop smarter, interconnected solutions.

5   Conclusion

Our study developed a Hybrid Distributed Information Retrieval (H-DIR) architecture in cloud IoT data centers, which significantly enhances data interoperability and analysis from diverse IoT sensors. By combining semantic web technologies, Big Data, and machine learning, the system improves both retrieval speed and accuracy. Its successful use in agricultural monitoring shows its versatility across different sectors. This work provides a scalable solution to the challenges of data heterogeneity in IoT systems, with future research aimed at expanding and refining the architecture's applications.

Acknowledgements. This work was supported in part by project SERICS (PE00000014) under the NRRP MUR program funded by the EU - NGEU.

References

1. Abdel-Basset, M., Shawky, L.A., Eldrandaly, K.: Grid quorum-based spatial coverage for IoT smart agriculture monitoring using enhanced multi-verse optimizer. Neural Comput. Appl. **32**, 607–624 (2020)
2. Al-Osta, M., Ahmed, B., Abdelouahed, G.: A lightweight semantic web-based approach for data annotation on IoT gateways. Procedia Comput. Sci. **113**, 186–193 (2017)
3. Androcec, D., Vrcek, N.: Thing as a service interoperability: review and framework proposal. In: 2016 IEEE 4th International Conference on Future Internet of Things and Cloud (FiCloud), pp. 309–316 (2016). https://api.semanticscholar.org/CorpusID:10086259
4. Anjana, P., Narayanamoorthi, M.: Secured natural language processing for conversion of unstructured text into structured intelligence. In: 2021 Second International Conference on Electronics and Sustainable Communication Systems (ICESC), pp. 957–962. IEEE (2021)
5. Armbrust, M., et al.: Spark SQL: relational data processing in spark. In: Proceedings of the 2015 ACM SIGMOD International Conference on Management of Data, pp. 1383–1394 (2015)

6. Astutik, Y., Murad, M., Putra, G.M.D., Setiawati, D.A.: Remote monitoring systems in greenhouse based on NodeMCU esp8266 microcontroller and android. In: AIP Conference Proceedings, vol. 2199. AIP Publishing (2019)
7. Bhamidipaty, A., Khabiri, E., Agrawal, B., Li, Y.: SiWare: contextual understanding of industrial data for situational awareness. In: Proceedings of the Thirty-Second International Joint Conference on Artificial Intelligence, pp. 7115–7118 (2023)
8. Duy, T.K., Quirchmayr, G., Tjoa, A., Hanh, H.H.: A semantic data model for the interpretion of environmental streaming data. In: 2017 Seventh International Conference on Information Science and Technology (ICIST), pp. 376–380. IEEE (2017)
9. Górka, W., Socha, M., Piasecki, A.: The use of D2RQ in the integration of development tools. Studia Ekonomiczne **308**, 62–73 (2016)
10. Hassan, M., Bansal, S.: Semantic data querying over NoSQL databases with apache spark. In: 2018 IEEE International Conference on Information Reuse and Integration (IRI), pp. 364–371 (2018). https://doi.org/10.1109/IRI.2018.00061
11. Hassan, M., Bansal, S.: S3QLRDF: distributed sparql query processing using apache spark-a comparative performance study. Distrib. Parallel Databases, 1–41 (2023). https://doi.org/10.1007/s10619-023-07422-4
12. Kamilaris, A., Gao, F., Prenafeta-Boldu, F.X., Ali, M.I.: Agri-IoT: a semantic framework for internet of things-enabled smart farming applications. In: 2016 IEEE 3rd World Forum on Internet of Things (WF-IoT), pp. 442–447. IEEE (2016)
13. Kang, Z., Huang, Z., Lu, C.: Speech enhancement using U-Net with compressed sensing. Appl. Sci. (2022). https://api.semanticscholar.org/CorpusID:248339213
14. Papernot, N., Abadi, M., Erlingsson, U., Goodfellow, I., Talwar, K.: Semi-supervised knowledge transfer for deep learning from private training data. arXiv preprint arXiv:1610.05755 (2016)
15. Qu, C., Tao, M., Zhang, J., Hong, X., Yuan, R.: A semantic web based intelligent IoT model. In: Vaidya, J., Li, J. (eds.) ICA3PP 2018. LNCS, vol. 11336, pp. 186–195. Springer, Cham (2018). https://doi.org/10.1007/978-3-030-05057-3_14
16. Sahay, M.R., Sukumaran, M.K., Amarnath, S., Palani, T.N.D.: Environmental monitoring system using iot and cloud service at real-time. EasyChair Preprint **5**(968), 1–8 (2019)
17. Salama, A., Shaheen, M.E., Al-Feel, H.: Semantic architecture for modelling and reasoning IoT data resources based on spark. Int. J. Adv. Comput. Sci. Appl. **11**(2), 431–438 (2020)
18. Samuel, K., et al.: Translating owl and semantic web rules into prolog: moving toward description logic programs. Theory Pract. Logic Program. **8**(3), 301–322 (2008)
19. Sharma, S., Sharma, A., Goel, T., Deoli, R., Mohan, S.: Smart home gardening management system: a cloud-based internet-of-things (IoT) application in VANET. In: 2020 11th International Conference on Computing, Communication and Networking Technologies (ICCCNT), pp. 1–5. IEEE (2020)
20. Shi, J., et al.: Generalized deep mixed models. In: Proceedings of the 28th ACM SIGKDD Conference on Knowledge Discovery and Data Mining, pp. 3869–3877 (2022)
21. Su, X., Zhang, H., Riekki, J., Keränen, A., Nurminen, J.K., Du, L.: Connecting IoT sensors to knowledge-based systems by transforming SenML to RDF. Procedia Comput. Sci. **32**, 215–222 (2014)
22. Vandana, C., Chikkamannur, A.A.: Semantic ontology based IoT-resource description. Int. J. Adv. Netw. Appl. **11**(1), 4184–4189 (2019)

23. Wan, J., Liu, J., Liao, L.: Guest editorial: special issue on "advanced artificial intelligence for industrial internet of things". J. Internet Technol. **21**(5), 1477–1478 (2020)
24. Wang, B., Kong, W., Guan, H., Xiong, N.N.: Air quality forecasting based on gated recurrent long short term memory model in internet of things. IEEE Access **7**, 69524–69534 (2019)
25. Wang, W., Barnaghi, P., Cassar, G., Ganz, F., Navaratnam, P.: Semantic sensor service networks. In: SENSORS, 2012 IEEE, pp. 1–4. IEEE (2012)
26. Xiao-lin, S.: Design and implementation of reasoning system based on description logic. J. Chin. Comput. Syst. **29**, 57–60 (2008)
27. Zhang, X., Zhao, Y., Liu, W.: Transforming sensor data to RDF based on SSN ontology. Adv. Sci. Technol. Lett. **81**, 95–98 (2015)

A Cyber-Physical Infrastructure for Smart Energy Buildings

Benoit Couraud[1,2](✉)🆔, Erwin Franquet[3]🆔, Honorat Quinard[1],
Pierre-Jean Barre[1], Paulo Moura[1]🆔, Yann Rozier[1], Franck Dechavanne[1],
Pierre Costini[1], Azeddine El Youssfi[1], Ahmad Taha[2]🆔, Sonam Norbu[2]🆔,
and David Flynn[2]🆔

[1] Université Côte d'Azur, IMREDD, Nice, France
benoit.couraud@glasgow.ac.uk
[2] James Watt School of Engineering, University of Glasgow, Glasgow, UK
[3] Université Côte d'Azur, Polytech'Lab, Nice, France

Abstract. The advancement of renewable energy and low carbon technologies, such as electric vehicles, necessitates that smart buildings adopt innovative energy use cases to become adaptive and responsive.

Additionally, the proliferation of Internet of Things (IoT) devices introduces new applications for enhancing comfort, air quality, health, and energy consumption. These evolutions require Building Automation Systems (BAS) to manage new devices and implement novel applications, which are often beyond the capabilities of current BAS technologies. Consequently, this paper proposes a Cyber-Physical Architecture that facilitates the integration of third-party IoT devices and the development of novel use cases. Specifically, the architecture supports the implementation of a Smart Energy Management System alongside standard BAS to optimize energy usage in smart buildings through IoT and artificial intelligence algorithms. The paper also presents a case study of the architecture's implementation in a smart building in Nice, France, and discusses the advantages and disadvantages of the proposed cyber-physical architecture for smart energy buildings.

Keywords: Cyber-Physical System · Smart buildings · Energy management system

1 Introduction

Since the early 1980s, building design and operation have significantly evolved with the introduction of digital systems for building automation through direct digital control [1]. Buildings have become smarter, integrating numerous sensors and advanced solutions for managing alarms, lighting, heating, air quality, and access control.

The integration of the Internet of Things (IoT) and Big Data Analysis has further enhanced building management, improving comfort and efficiency. The

© IFIP International Federation for Information Processing 2025
Published by Springer Nature Switzerland AG 2025
G. Rey et al. (Eds.): IFIPIoT 2024, IFIP AICT 738, pp. 22–29, 2025.
https://doi.org/10.1007/978-3-031-82065-6_3

deployment of renewable energy and low-carbon technologies, such as solar photovoltaic (PV) systems and electric vehicles (EVs), has transformed buildings into complex energy systems. These systems require new control algorithms to optimize energy use, reduce costs, and decrease carbon footprints. Consequently, today's smart buildings require not only traditional Building Automation Systems but also optimized Energy Management Systems (EMS).

Additionally, smart buildings are increasingly incorporating advanced digital technologies like sensors, actuators, and AI-based services. These enhance real-time control but also introduce new vulnerabilities, including potential cyber-attacks. As a result, buildings are evolving into Cyber-Physical Energy Systems, which demand innovative design and control strategies [2–4]. Cyber-Physical Systems (CPS) integrate cyber infrastructure-including communication systems, software, and control algorithms-with physical assets like sensors, actuators, and energy networks [5]. These systems enable efficient operation through interaction and communication between various physical and cyber components [6]. However, this integration poses challenges in maintaining reliable, safe, and secure operations [7].

Historically, smart buildings relied on dedicated networks linking sensors, actuators, and controllers, all integrated by building automation companies to ensure compatibility. Control algorithms were typically implemented in programmable logic controllers with limited capabilities compared to advanced methods like Model Predictive Control [8], fuzzy logic, or AI-based optimization algorithms. Recent advancements in IoT, big data analysis, and control algorithms have enabled new use cases, such as optimizing ventilation based on air quality forecasts. Implementing these use cases requires expanding traditional Building Automation Systems to include a broader range of devices and controllers capable of AI-based optimization, highlighting the need for new architectures that maintain reliability, robustness, and security.

This paper presents a CPS architecture for smart buildings that integrates standard building automation systems with low-carbon technologies, such as renewable energy and electric vehicles. It builds on standard IIoT layered architectures [9] and on Smart Grid Architecture Model [10] and proposes to merge these approaches with a Service Oriented Architecture (SOA) that enables to better separate the tasks and enable an easier maintenance of smart building systems. This architecture addresses the diverse devices, protocols, and use cases introduced by IoT and AI developments. This paper also presents a concrete implementation of such architecture, which ensures replication of the approach proposed in this work. The paper is structured as follows: Sect. 2 proposes a general architecture for Cyber-Physical Building Energy Systems, Sect. 3 describes a case study implementation in a smart building in southeastern France, and Sect. 4 discusses future developments for integrated cyber-physical infrastructure in smart buildings.

2 Cyber-Physical Building Energy Systems

With the rise of smart buildings, new functions and services have emerged, necessitating changes in design and operation. Buildings are now integral to the local energy system, incorporating renewable energy production, electric vehicle (EV) integration, and supporting the electricity grid. While energy-plus buildings often focus on large-scale renewable energy and efficient consumption, many lack operational control for enhanced resilience and efficiency [11]. For example, smart EV-charging can shift demand to periods of high production, reducing grid stress during peak times.

Building operation now also emphasizes occupant comfort, requiring the integration of sensors and complex control strategies, often managed remotely via cloud services. Additionally, reducing operational costs has become a priority, with new energy savings performance contracts necessitating actions like demand shifting and enhanced user interfaces. To address these needs, an adapted Cyber-Physical System (CPS) architecture is proposed to detail the interactions between specific services. The proposed CPS architecture builds on traditional architectures such as the multi-layered Reference architectural model industrie 4.0 proposed in [9], and integrates a Service Oriented Architecture for the application layer that is split between the expert applications, that include Building Automation Systems (BAS), Smart Energy Management System (SEMS), and Air Quality Management System (AQMS), and support applications such as digital services for forecasting, clustering and standard data analysis (Fig. 1).

- Assets layer: This architecture includes the assets layer, with standard BAS related assets (lighting, HVAC, access control, fire systems, and sensors), but also assets related to other applications as energy related assets (heat pumps and EV chargers), not historically managed by BAS. Devices can be controlled by the BAS or specific applications, depending on technical needs.
- Integration Layer: The assets are integrated within the building through the integration layer with communication devices able to connect devices to the local or wide area network.
- Communication layer: Devices communicate to the applications through the communication layer, that includes the possibility for certain devices to send data to cloud services, necessitating local data retrieval services in the support applications layer. Therefore, devices can send data to local storage directly, or use cloud-based APIs due to manufacturers' designs. Communication protocols include ModBus, BACnet, KNX, Zigbee, LoRa and others, with gateways linking these to broader networks. Also, this layer includes cyber-security which is critical for CPBES, given the need for interaction with third-party platforms and internet-connected devices. Common vulnerabilities include command injection, Cross site request forgery (CSRF), default credentials, and authentication bypass. Mitigation strategies include secure design practices, strong password policies, secure remote access, and regular security audits.

– Information layer: The information layer includes visualization, data models conversion and data storage. The data storage facility should employ standard models like FIWARE, Brick, or Haystack to ensure interoperability.
– Expert Applications layer: Devices control is typically centralized through the BAS, though some devices may be directly managed by specific applications like the SEMS. In this architecture, core applications such as BAS, SEMS, and AQMS manage specific devices by collecting data and implementing control algorithms. As an example, SEMS optimizes energy consumption and production, focusing on self-consumption of renewable energy and load shifting. AQMS manages air quality, using sensors to optimize ventilation and heating. Additional services can follow this model, leveraging sensors and AI for optimized control.
– Support Applications layer: Digital services, including predictive maintenance and forecasting, enhance building management by utilizing data from integrated sensors. Forecasting is crucial for optimizing operations, such as EV charging and air quality management. A typical workflow for these services involves data cleaning, model selection, and forecast generation.

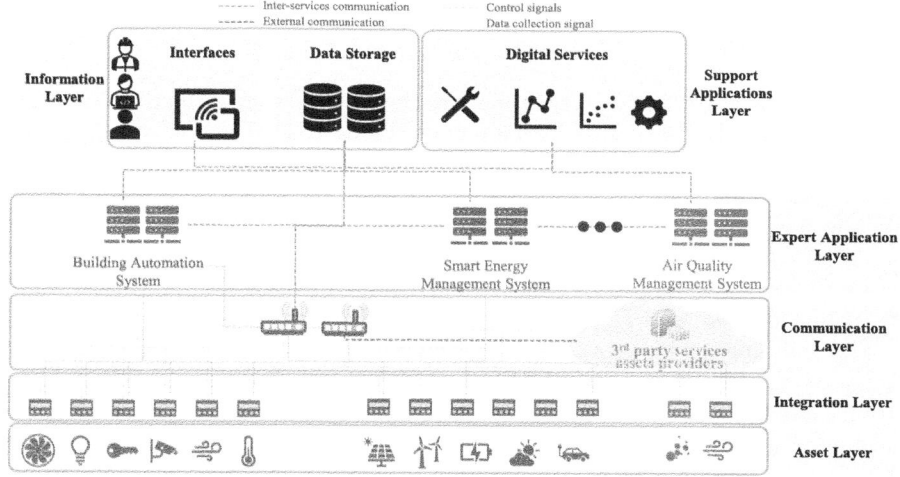

Fig. 1. General Architecture of a CPBES.

3   An Example of Cyber-Physical Building Energy Systems

Section 2 described the architecture for Cyber-Physical Building Energy Systems (CPBES). Here, we present an example of this architecture implemented

Fig. 2. IMREDD Building implementing the CPBES, including a view from the roof and showroom overview.

in a building located in Nice, operated by the Mediterranean Institute of Risk, Environment and Sustainable Development (IMREDD) (Fig. 2).

The IMREDD building, located in Nice Meridia, is an energy-positive demonstrator producing more energy annually than it consumes. It features a 180 kW photovoltaic plant and two wind turbines on the roof. Heating and cooling are provided by a geothermal loop circulating through the Méridia eco-neighborhood. The building's daily energy demand ranges from 18 kW to 40 kW, primarily due to HVAC systems and IT infrastructure.

The building includes a 182 kWh battery system controlled by a Smart Energy Management System (SEMS) to store excess solar energy and discharge during peak electricity prices. It also has 18 EV charging points, making smart charging essential to avoid exceeding the building's transformer capacity. Over 70 indoor air quality sensors are installed to monitor environmental conditions (Fig. 3).

The IMREDD building employs the proposed CPBES architecture, with the Building Automation System (BAS) by Schneider Electric at its core. BAS controls ventilation, lighting, and valve systems using several communication protocols (BACnet, KNX, ...). The SEMS manages energy-related appliances, communicating primarily via Modbus TCP/IP, with specific protocols for EVs. The real-time control algorithm of SEMS optimizes battery use based on real-time and forecasted data, implemented in Python and Node-RED. The Air Quality Management System (AQMS) uses LoRa sensors for indoor air quality monitoring, with actions routed through the BAS. Data storage is managed using

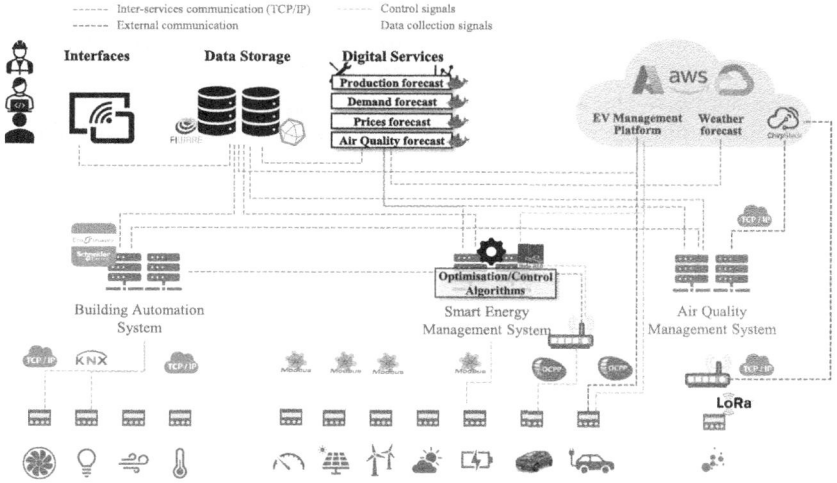

Fig. 3. CPBES architecture implementation for IMREDD Building.

InfluxDB and a Fiware NGSI-LD database to ensure data interoperability. Forecasting services were implemented to predict day-ahead electricity consumption and production using lightweight AI models such as k-nearest neighbors (kNN), XGBoost, and ANNs. These models are trained on reduced datasets for improved processing time and accuracy, achieving over 92% accuracy (R^2) for the next 24 h demand forecasts. Forecasting services are deployed via Docker Compose, enhancing deployment efficiency and compatibility.

4   Discussion

The proposed Cyber-Physical Building Energy System (CPBES) aims to provide an architecture that better integrates secondary applications (energy management, air quality management, ...) into the standard operations of buildings by proposing a service oriented architecture (SOA). This allows a better distribution of computing power and a better maintenance of the system. Challenges include scalability, diverse data formats, and cybersecurity threats. The service-oriented architecture of CPBES offers flexible integration of sensors and actuators, but certain issues still require attention.

The modular CPBES allows adding services as needed while maintaining clear interfaces to avoid overlap. A well-defined SOA promotes independence, reusability, and interoperability. Without well-defined boundaries, the system could become complex and unmanageable. Therefore, clear interfaces and modularity must be enforced to prevent "spaghetti code."

To integrate various sensors, an interoperability layer is crucial, avoiding the need for unique connectors for each sensor. Adopting smart data models like SAREF allows integration of different devices. This flexibility enables real-time adaptation of the energy management systems, enhancing comfort and optimizing energy efficiency by adjusting to real-time data. Including end-users in sensor deployment improves data coverage and system adaptability.

CPBES supports the addition of application services for new use cases, such as integrating buildings into the electric grid. Smart buildings can aid grid regulation by responding to tariff signals and managing demand via the Smart Energy Management System (SEMS). With the rise of EVs, V2G systems, and storage technologies, better management of energy within neighborhoods and communities is needed. The CPBES enables smart buildings to contribute to local energy markets and community requirements.

CPBES must evolve to account for interactions with end-users, transitioning from cyber-physical to symbiotic systems. Further research is needed to optimize these interactions, ensuring user interfaces dynamically adapt to preferences. Reinforcement learning can be used to adjust to user comfort preferences over time. Transparency in control decisions, compliance with GDPR, and user empowerment are critical. Engaging users in managing flexible assets enhances the adoption of smart building technologies and fosters sustainable behaviors. Trust and ethical practices are essential for the social acceptance of AI within these systems.

5   Conclusion

The integration of IoT devices into buildings paves the way for their integration into Building Automation Systems (BAS) to take control decisions. The challenge is that BAS usually relies on specific devices that are compatible and approved by the existing control software. As a result, the deployment of IoT devices leads to interoperability challenges as well as security threat, as some IoT devices might not be secure by design. Similarly, buildings are becoming complex energy systems able to optimise their consumption and production to reduce their bill and provide services to the energy system. However, such new use cases require new control rules and integration of optimisation and AI based algorithms to better coordinate the assets of smart buildings. This requires a new way of designing BAS. This paper proposes a Cyber-Physical Architecture for buildings that integrate renewable energy and low carbon assets such as EVs or heat pumps. It merges standard multi-layered architectures with Service Oriented Architecture and splits applications between expert and support applications to improve the distribution of computing power and to ease the maintenance of the system. Therefore, the architecture proposes a digital concierge, that provides digital services to all applications, such as forecasting, clustering or optimisation that can run on dedicated hardware. This cyber-physical infrastructure was implemented in a smart building in Nice with success of operation, as all applications are running in parallel seamlessly, optimising energy consumption and production as well as air quality. The next step will include the evolution from a cyber-physical infrastructure to a symbiotic building energy system that integrates end-users in the building's operations.

Acknowledgments. The authors acknowledge the support of the Smart City Innovation Center, funded by the european union, Dpartemebt des Alpes Maritimes, Rgion Sud Provence Alpes Cte d'Azur and the Initiative dExcellence du Programme Investissements dAvenir program; the UK Engineering and Physical Sciences Council (EPSRC), through Hydrogen Integration for Accelerated Energy Transitions Hub (HI-ACT) project [EP/X038823/1] and DecarbonISation PAThways for Cooling and Heating (DISPATCH) project [EP/V042955/1].

References

1. Bell, S.V., Murray, T.M., Duncan, K.T.: Design of direct digital control systems for building control and facilities management. In: IEEE Proceedings of the SOUTHEASTCON 1991, vol. 2, pp. 674–676 (1991)
2. Smeenk, H.G., Petock, M.: Internet of Things for Smart Buildings: Leverage IoT for smarter insights for buildings in the new and built environments (2023)
3. Havard, N., McGrath, S., Flanagan, C., MacNamee, C.: Smart building based on internet of things technology. In: 2018 12th International Conference on Sensing Technology (ICST), pp. 278–281 (2018)
4. Bajer, M.: Iot for smart buildings - long awaited revolution or lean evolution. In: 2018 IEEE 6th International Conference on Future Internet of Things and Cloud (FiCloud), pp. 149–154 (2018)
5. Alvarez-Alvarado, M.S., Apolo-Tinoco, C.: Cyber-physical power systems: a comprehensive review about technologies drivers, standards, and future perspectives. Comput. Electr. Eng. **116**, 109149 (2024)
6. Agostinelli, S., Cumo, F., Guidi, G., Tomazzoli, C.: Cyber-physical systems improving building energy management: digital twin and artificial intelligence. Energies **14**(8), 2338 (2021)
7. Bobis, C.H.G., Barrion, C.M., Villaluna, J.G., Onte, D.C.V., Peralta, J.F., Sangalang, R.G.B.: A smart building design using cyber-physical system modeling. In: 2023 International Conference for Advancement in Technology (ICONAT), pp. 1–8 (2023)
8. Karbasi, A., Farhadi, A.: A cyber-physical system for building automation and control based on a distributed MPC with an efficient method for communication. Eur. J. Control. **61**, 151–170 (2021)
9. Schweichhart, K.: Reference architectural model industrie 4.0 (RAMI 4.0). An Introduction, 40 (2016)
10. Smart grid reference architecture. Technical report, CEN-CENELEC-ETSI Smart grid coordination group (2012)
11. Osma, G., Amado, L., Villamizar, R., Ordoñez, G.: Building automation systems as tool to improve the resilience from energy behavior approach. Procedia Eng. **118**, 861–868 (2015)

GRAAL4IoT'24: First International workshop on the DesiGn, VeRificAtion, and VALidation of IoT Systems

SINDIT: A Framework for Knowledge Graph-Based Digital Twins in Smart Manufacturing

An Ngoc Lam[1(✉)], Gøran Brekke Svaland[1], Miguel Ángel Barcelona[2],
Shane Keaveney[3], Wissam Mallouli[4], Luong Nguyen[4], Assia Belbachir[5],
Xiang Ma[1], Akhilesh Kumar Srivastava[1], and Ahmed Nabil Belbachir[5]

[1] SINTEF AS, Oslo, Norway
{an.lam,goran.svaland,xiang.ma,akhilesh.srivastava}@sintef.no
[2] Instituto Tecnológico de Aragón, Zaragoza, Spain
mabarcelona@ita.es
[3] Croom Medical, Croom, Co., Limerick, Ireland
shane@croommedical.com
[4] Montimage, Paris, France
{wissam.mallouli,luong.nguyen}@montimage.com
[5] NORCE Norwegian Research Centre, Grimstad, Norway
{assb,nabe}@norceresearch.no

Abstract. Digital twins are revolutionizing smart manufacturing by facilitating real-time monitoring, simulation, and optimization of physical processes. This paper introduces the SINDIT framework, a comprehensive approach tailored for developing knowledge graph-based digital twins. By seamlessly integrating cognitive capabilities, SINDIT enhances decision-making and operational efficiency within manufacturing systems. Central to its architecture is a robust data pipeline, adept at organizing and linking vast amounts of heterogeneous data, thereby enabling advanced data analytics and reasoning.

Case studies from the pilots of the COGNIMAN project underscore the practical utility and benefits of the SINDIT framework. These studies showcase notable enhancements in predictive maintenance, process optimization, and overall productivity. By harnessing the power of knowledge graphs and cognitive capabilities, SINDIT represents a promising avenue for driving innovation and efficiency in smart manufacturing. Through this framework, manufacturers can achieve a higher level of operational insight and agility, leading to improved performance and competitiveness in the market.

Keywords: Digital Twins · Industry 4.0 · Smart Manufacturing

1 Introduction

The advent of Industry 4.0 has marked the beginning of a new era in smart manufacturing, characterized by the seamless integration of advanced digital

G. Rey et al. (Eds.): IFIPIoT 2024, IFIP AICT 738, pp. 33–52, 2025.
https://doi.org/10.1007/978-3-031-82065-6_4

technologies and physical production processes [7]. Among these technologies, Digital Twins (DTs) have emerged as a pivotal innovation, providing real-time virtual representation of physical systems [21]. By leveraging DTs, manufacturers can monitor, simulate, and optimize their operations, leading to enhanced productivity, efficiency, and decision-making capabilities [25].

Despite the significant potential of DTs, there is a pressing need for tools that simplify their development and deployment. As defined in [6], a DT software platform includes various components such as IoT connections for communication with the physical twins, data integration, processing and persistence, development of the DT information model, evaluation of DT algorithms (e.g., data-driven analytics), conducting simulations, and visualization of the DT models and analytic results. Existing DT solutions in the market, such as Azure Digital Twins [13], Amazon TwinMaker [1] and ThingWorx [17] are highly customized and proprietary. While open-source solutions such as Thingsboard [23], Asset Administration Shell (AAS) [3], or Eclipse Ditto [4] and Vorto [5] exist, they are tailored to support only specific steps in the development of a DT. An integrated framework that seamlessly brings these components together to enable an end-to-end DT system is still lacking.

To address these limitations, we aim to extend our previous work [25] and present SINDIT (**SINTEF DI**gital **T**win) as an open-source DT framework that is more flexible and maintainable. SINDIT will support continuous development to be applicable to various use cases in the smart manufacturing domain. Our primary objective is to create a modular and scalable framework that simplifies the development and deployment of DTs. The proposed framework will feature:

- **Flexible Data Integration**: Support for a wide variety of data sources and communication protocols, making it easy to connect to different physical systems.
- **Scalable Data Model**: A generic information model that can handle heterogeneous datasets and diverse types of data, ensuring compatibility and extensibility.
- **Knowledge Graph Integration**: The use of knowledge graphs to provide a comprehensive and interconnected representation of the DT, enhancing data integration, querying, and reasoning capabilities.
- **Modular Architecture**: A four-layer architecture (Data, DT Representation, Service and User Interface) that ensures seamless integration of components, enabling end-to-end development of DTs.

The practical application and validation of the SINDIT framework are demonstrated through its implementation in various use cases. For instance, the DT of the Fischertechnik factory showcases real-time monitoring and anomaly detection, while the COGNIMAN project[1] involves pilots in precision machining and additive manufacturing, highlighting significant potential for improvements in decision-making and operational efficiency.

---

[1] https://cogniman.eu/.

This paper is organized as follows: Sect. 2 provides background information on the COGNIMAN project and the state-of-the-art development of DT frameworks. Section 3 details the SINDIT framework, including its architecture and implementation. Section 4 discusses the use cases and pilot applications of the framework in smart manufacturing environments. Finally, Sect. 5 concludes the paper and outlines future work.

2 Background

2.1 COGNIMAN COGNitive Industries for Smart MANufacturing

The COGNIMAN project aims to revolutionize manufacturing through the development and deployment of AI-enhanced robotic systems designed for flexibility, modularity, reasoning, and decision-making. The primary objective is to create a scalable, modular solution that enables quick early adoption in various manufacturing processes that have traditionally been difficult to automate. This involves defining a virtual/simulation platform architecture with highly flexible, reconfigurable, and controllable production for digital cognitive manufacturing.

New technologies play a crucial role in COGNIMAN, particularly DTs, AI, and human-in-the-loop systems. DTs are used for parameter optimization prior to deployment, significantly reducing the validation effort. AI technologies are integrated to provide real-time decision-making capabilities and self-adaptiveness to changing conditions. The human-in-the-loop approach ensures that the developed systems are user-friendly and ergonomic, enhancing safety and collaboration between human operators and robots. This combination aims to foster a seamless integration of advanced technologies in manufacturing environments.

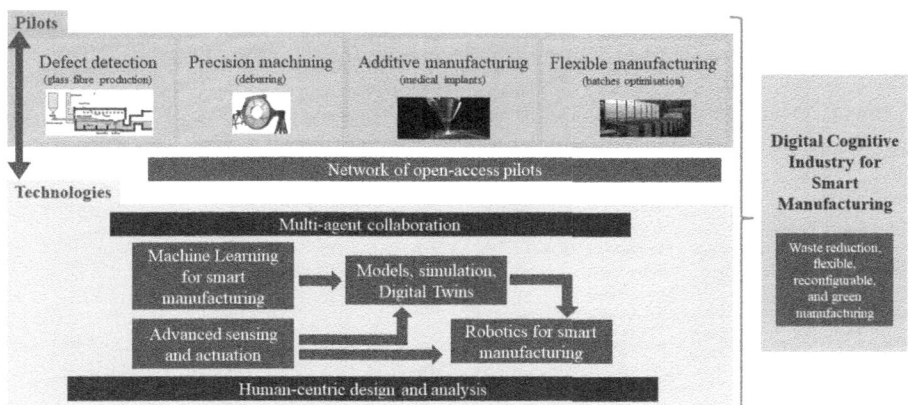

Fig. 1. The COGNIMAN Big picture

COGNIMAN includes four pilot projects to demonstrate the applicability of its technologies. These pilots involve validation in real manufacturing environments to ensure the integrated system works effectively. The pilots cover various manufacturing scenarios: defect detection in fiberglass production, precision machining for deburring large metal parts, additive manufacturing for medical implants, and creating a digital library for batch management in flexible manufacturing. As will be described in the following sections, SINDIT will be specifically used for two of these pilots. The ultimate goal is to create a comprehensive toolbox for smart manufacturing, integrating simulation, models, DTs, AI, sensors, and robotics into a modular solution to automate processes, improve decision-making, and enhance operational efficiency.

2.2 Digital Twin Frameworks

Digital Twins (DTs) are digital representations of physical systems, where physical assets, processes and their relationships are modelled to not only replicate the conditions and status of the physical twin system, but to extend and enhance the system with predictive analysis for future events and simulations of what-if scenarios [25]. There are several actors on the market providing frameworks for building, hosting and managing DT systems. In Table 1, we have listed several proprietary and opensource software systems. The table shows whether the software provides capabilities of remote procedure calls, what data source protocols are supported, and what programming language interface is provided by the software to perform data analytics. On the other hand, in some cases data can be exported to other services that perform the analytics and store the results, that in turn the DT software can consume. A major difference between the proprietary solutions and the opensource solutions are vendor *lock-in* -effects. To make use of the DT service, other services from the same software provider might be required for example to obtain IoT data, perform analytics or to build machine learning models. Opensource frameworks are, in this regard, more customizable, but on the flip side these typically require more of the user to build a fully functioning DT.

Table 1. Overview of various digital twin software solutions. 🏠 ☁ ☁⬆: Hosting on-premise, cloud or possibility to upload models to cloud based hosting, respectively.

Software	Pricing model	Open source	Hosting	Remote control	Data sources	Analytics language
Azure Digital Twins [13]	Pay by use	no	☁	✗	Azure IoT services	
Amazon TwinMaker [1]	Tier based pay by use	no	☁	✗	AWS IoT services	
Ansys Twin Builder [2]	Licence based	no	🏠☁⬆	?	?	
ThingWorx [17]	Licence based	no	🏠☁⬆	?	?	
Insights Hub [20]	Licence based	no	🏠☁	✓	MQTT, OPC-UA	
ThingsBoard Professional [23]	Tier based	Apache 2.0	🏠☁	✓	MQTT, OPC-UA, HTTPS REST, FTP, SNMP, ODBC	Python
ThingsBoard Community	Free	Apache 2.0	🏠	✓	MQTT, OPC-UA, HTTPS REST, FTP, SNMP, ODBC	Python
DTaaS [22]	Free	GPL v3	🏠	?	MQTT, RabbitMQ InfluxDB, MongoDB	
SMOL [8]	Free	BSD-3-Clause	🏠	✗	?	SMOL, FMO
Asset Administration Shell [3]	Free	CC-BY-4	🏠	✓	OPC-UA	
Eclipse Ditto [4] + Eclipse Vorto [5]	Free	EPL v2	🏠	✗	MQTT, AMQP, HTTP, Kafka	
SINDIT [25]	Free	MIT	🏠	✗	MQTT, OPC-UA, InfluxDB	

3   SINDIT Knowledge Graph Based DT Framework

3.1   Software Architecture

SINDIT is structured according to the reference architecture for DT systems developed in COGNIMAN project. It aims to enhance flexibility and modularity through interfaces to connect different components for the purpose of building knowledge graph based DTs. Figure 2 depicts the four-layer architecture of SINDIT along with its constituent components.

Physical Twin. The Physical Twin refers to real-world physical assets that are replicated and modeled as DTs within virtual environments. Physical twins can be tangible objects such as sensors, actuators, machinery, or equipment which are monitored during the production in the factory. They can also include intangible artifacts such as processes that need optimization or software systems used in operations. They can even extend to human DTs [24], which represent individuals in virtual form, facilitating personalized simulations, health monitoring, and performance optimization of the operators in the manufacturing environment.

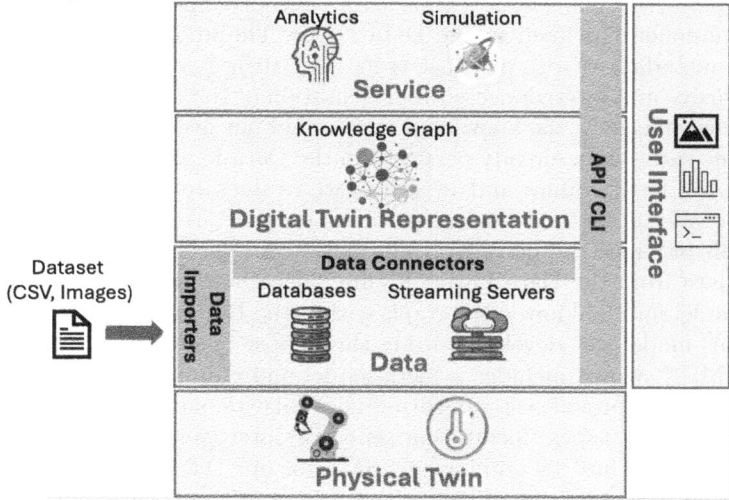

Fig. 2. SINDIT Software Architecture.

Data Layer. To interact with DTs, physical twins need to provide interfaces for the collection of data necessary for building their virtual representations and for receiving the control feedback from the DT. This can be achieved by using *data streaming servers* that support bidirectional communication, such as OPC-UA [11], MQTT [18], or RESTful [12] APIs. The Data Layer contains the software components that handle interaction with the physical twins, supporting the collection, storage, and management of data generated by them. It also includes various *databases* to persist the generated data. Additionally, for physical systems that can only export historical datasets manually, the Data Layer provides *Data Importers* to onboard these datasets into its internal databases. The *Data Connectors* are the critical components to make data available to the higher layer. Data Connectors provide a standardized interface to access the data, regardless of the underlying databases and streaming servers. Furthermore, new data connectors can be dynamically registered to support new communication protocols or new database systems employed by the physical twins. Similarly, whenever physical systems generate datasets with a new data format, a new implementation of the corresponding data importer can be added to the Data Layer. This solution enables loose coupling between the layers and among the components, thereby enhancing the modularity and flexibility of the framework.

Digital Twin Representation Layer. The Digital Twin Representation Layer employs the *Knowledge Graph* as a conceptualization layer, integrating all the components defined in the Data Layer. The knowledge graph incorporates the metadata of the physical twins and their relationships, providing a comprehensive and interconnected representation of the DT. For scalability and performance efficiency, the knowledge graph does not necessarily contain all historical time-series data already persisted in the Data Layer. Instead, it may capture only the latest values and/or aggregated values (e.g., average, minimum, maximum values) for real-time monitoring purpose. Additionally, the knowledge graph provides the necessary information for the higher layer to retrieve detailed data from the Data Layer. Figure 3 depicts an excerpt from the information model for the knowledge graph within the Digital Twin Representation Layer. This model was developed using the Eclipse Semantic Modelling Framework (ESMF)[2], which includes a meta-model and editor tailored for DT modeling. ESMF also provides standardized vocabularies, such as those for units of measure and data types, facilitating semantic interoperability across different DT frameworks. Thus, by employing ESMF for our DT solution, our goal is to ensure a robust and interoperable representation of our DT system.

---

[2] https://eclipse-esmf.github.io/.

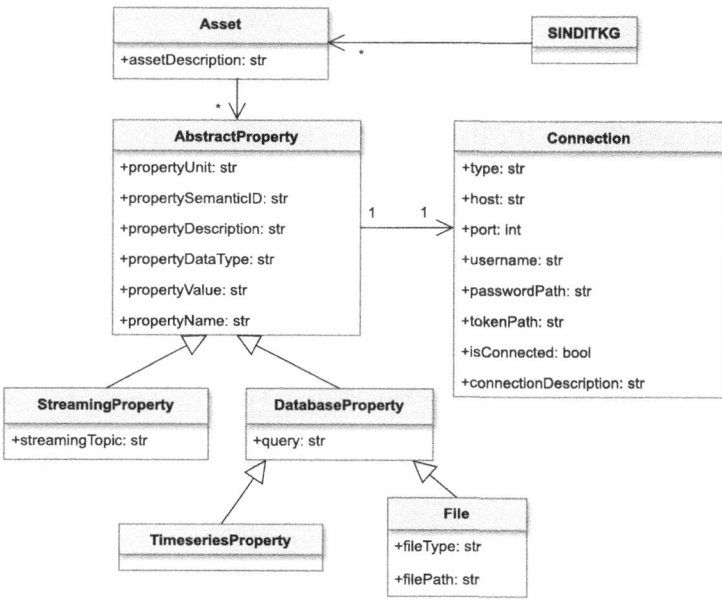

Fig. 3. SINDIT Knowledge Graph Information Model.

As depicted in Fig. 3, the *SINDIT Knowledge Graph (SINDITKG)* consists of different *Assets*, which represents the physical devices in the Physical Twins. Each asset may have different *Abstract Properties*, which can be either quantitative (with *Unit* and *Data Type*) or qualitative values. The *Semantic ID* attribute of these properties refers to an externally defined standardized vocabulary that explains the precise semantic interpretation of the data value. Examples of such vocabularies include the IEC 61360 - Common Data Dictionary[3] for electric/electronic devices and ECLASS[4] for data across various industrial domains. The Semantic ID can also reference a concept defined in other domain-specific OWL ontologies, ensuring comprehensive semantic interoperability within the framework. The *Property Value* attribute maintains the observed value of the property. As previously mentioned, this could represent either the latest observation or accumulated values derived from time-series data.

The *Connection* class within the information model contains details necessary to establish a connection to the underlying database or streaming server. This connection is utilized for instantiating a new Data Connector to the Data Layer. For security reasons, the knowledge graph does not store any credential information (such as passwords or access tokens); instead, it includes paths to external secret vaults where this sensitive information is securely stored.

---

[3] https://cdd.iec.ch/.
[4] https://eclass.eu.

In addition to the Abstract Property, the information model also includes several concrete properties. The *Streaming Property* facilitates real-time data retrieval from a streaming server, with the Streaming Topic attribute specifying the identifier of the value on the server (e.g., the topic in an MQTT server or the node path in an OPC-UA server). The *Database Property* represents a data value stored within a database system (e.g., a measurement in a time-series database or a column in a relational table), with a query used to retrieve that specific value from the database. Additionally, the *Timeseries Property* and *File Property* denote a continuous value or an object stored in a time-series database or file system, respectively.

Service Layer. The Service Layer comprises the functionalities that leverage the data and representation in the Digital Twin Representation and Data Layers to provides various data-driven services. This layer is structured on modular principles, allowing different components to be integrated using standardized APIs provided by the underlying Digital Twin Representation layer. Examples of these services can include:

- Analytics: Performs data analysis to derive insights and predictions.
- Simulation: Conducts simulations to predict outcomes and test scenarios.
- Graph-based Reasoning: Utilizes logical inference and rule-based systems to make decisions and recommendations based on data from the graph.
- Monitoring: Continuously access and update data from the knowledge graph to detect anomalies or deviations from expected norms.
- Control: Uses insights derived from analytics and simulations to automate actions and optimize operations in real-time.

These capabilities leverage the integrated data from the Digital Twin Representation Layer to enhance decision-making and operational efficiencies across diverse applications and industries.

User Interface. The three layers - Data, Digital Twin Representation, and Service - not only provide APIs and CLI for internal communication but also facilitate seamless integration with external systems and applications. The User Interface Layer leverages these interfaces to enhance user interaction. It utilizes APIs and CLI to offer intuitive interfaces for users to interact with DT functionalities. This includes visualizing real-time data, configuring simulations, evaluating different ML models, accessing analytical insights, modifying the knowledge graph to add new assets, controlling the physical devices, and configuring connections through user-friendly dashboards and controls.

3.2 Implementation and Deployment

The implementation and deployment of the SINDIT framework focus on ensuring modularity, scalability, and ease of integration with various data sources and systems. To facilitate rapid prototyping and deployment, the SINDIT framework is containerized using Docker, enabling different components to be deployed as separate containers. Key components include:

Data Layer. This layer contains the components supporting bi-directional interaction with the Physical Twins and persisting the generated data. The current version of SINDIT includes components that support MQTT and OPCUA servers. For data storage, it employs InfluxDB[5] for time series data and MinIO[6] for object data such as documents and images. As mentioned earlier, the Data Layer is designed to be easily extended to support different databases or communication protocols. Accordingly, we proposed a unified interface for each type of communication (e.g., to retrieve the database, to interact with the streaming server) so that the integration of new systems is streamlined. This modular design allows for the seamless addition of new functionalities without disrupting existing operations.

For the secret vault, HashiCorp Vault[7] is employed. However, similar to other types of databases, new technologies for secret storage can also be integrated as long as an adapter that implements the secret vault interface is available. This ensures that sensitive information, such as credentials and private keys, is securely stored and managed.

Digital Twin Representation Layer. This layer employs a Knowledge Graph to integrate all components defined in the Data Layer, capturing the metadata of the physical twins and their relationships. GraphDB[8]-an RDF triplestore which has shown decent performance as benchmarked in [10]-is employed to store and manage the knowledge graph data within the Digital Twin Representation Layer. Most RDF triplestores provide a SPARQL endpoint, which is a standardized HTTP protocol to query and update semantic knowledge graphs using SPARQL syntax. Consequently, other triplestores can be easily integrated into the Digital Twin Representation Layer, enabling flexibility and adaptability of the system. This ensures that the knowledge graph can evolve with emerging technologies and changing requirements, providing a robust foundation for advanced data analytics and reasoning within the SINDIT framework.

Service and User Interface Layers. These two layers are currently highly application-specific, tailored to meet the precise needs of various use cases. Accordingly, we have different components and dashboards developed for these use cases as described in [25]. Our immediate focus is to ensure that the framework meets the specific requirements of different manufacturing environments, providing optimal performance and relevance.

---

[5] https://www.influxdata.com/.
[6] https://min.io/.
[7] https://www.hashicorp.com/products/vault.
[8] https://graphdb.ontotext.com/.

Looking ahead, our vision is to transform this layer into a more generic and versatile toolkit. Future developments will include a range of machine learning models, enabling users to easily evaluate and deploy these models. This will provide a modular and flexible suite of tools, allowing users to customize and extend the functionalities of the SINDIT framework.

Moreover, similar to the design strategy in the Data Layer, we plan to develop unified interfaces to integrate various simulation technologies and retrieve results from analytics and simulations seamlessly. This standardization will facilitate smoother integration and interoperability, streamline the development of user interfaces, and allow users to leverage advanced simulation and analytical tools without extensive customization efforts.

The SINDIT open-source prototype, written in Python, can be found on the GitHub repository[9], along with a use case for the Fischertechnik Factory. It is also being adapted for two pilots in the COGNIMAN project, specifically within the domains of precision machining and additive manufacturing. Details about these use cases will be discussed in the next section.

4   Use Cases

In this section, we describe the application of the SINDIT framework. The digital twin of the Fischertechnik factory is already implemented, showcasing real-time monitoring and anomaly detection. Additionally, we outline the vision for applying SINDIT in two COGNIMAN pilots: precision machining and additive manufacturing, aimed at enhancing decision-making and efficiency.

4.1   Digital Twin of the Fischertechnik Factory

This section describes the implementation of the DT for the Fischertechnik factory[10], a fully realized application of SINDIT framework. This training factory simulates Industry 4.0 processes, incorporating a high-bay warehouse, a multi-processing station, a sorting line with color recognition, an environmental station with various sensors and surveillance camera, a delivery and pickup station with colour detection and NFC reader, and a vacuum suction gripper robot. These physical components constantly send sensor data to the DT through MQTT and OPC-UA servers. The list of 37 sensor values is described in Table 2.

---

[9] https://github.com/SINTEF-9012/SINDIT.
[10] https://www.fischertechnik.de.

Table 2. Sensor data collected from the Fischertechnik Factory.

Physical Devices	Sensor Values	Streaming Protocol
Environment Sensor	14 values for temperature, humidity, air quality and pressure, camera positions and its image	MQTT
Muti-Processing Station (MPO)	2 values for MPO status	OPC-UA
Sorting Line (SLD)	2 values for SLD status	OPC-UA
Highbay Warehouse (HBW)	6 values for HBW status and positions	MQTT
Delivery and Pickup (DPS)	4 values for DPS status	OPC-UA
Robot (VGR)	9 values for VGR status and positions	OPC-UA

The Data Layer of the Fischertechnik DT includes Data Connectors for both MQTT and OPC-UA to provide real-time data retrieval. Additionally, this layer also incorporates an InfluxDB database to store historical sensor values from these two streaming servers, as well as MinIO to store object files such as images taken from the camera, CAD images, and manuals for the physical devices.

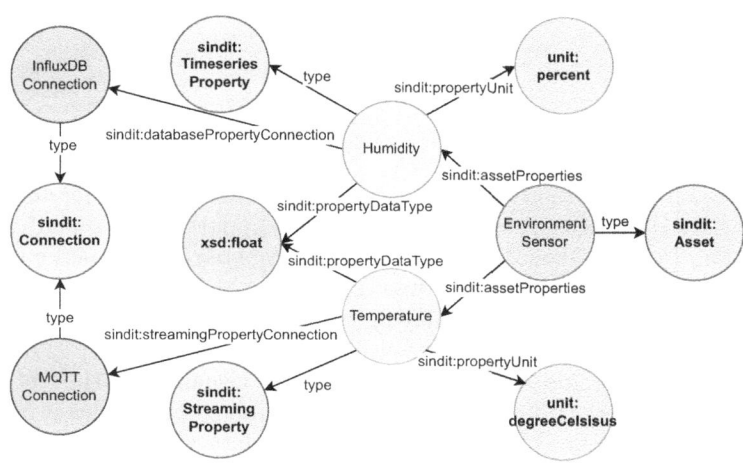

Fig. 4. Snapshot of the SINDIT subgraph for the Fischertechnik factory. Bold nodes are defined in the SINDIT information model; others are the factory instances.

Figure 4 illustrates a subgraph of the Digital Twin Representation Layer where the metadata (e.g., data type, units of measure, connection details) of the humidity and temperature sensor values are captured by the graph. As described in Sect. 3, the attributes (also known as data properties) of the nodes (e.g., credential information of the connection, data values of the properties) are also captured in the knowledge graph. These attributes can be used to retrieve more data from the Data Layers, such as by instantiating new Data Connectors to the MQTT or InfluxDB servers.

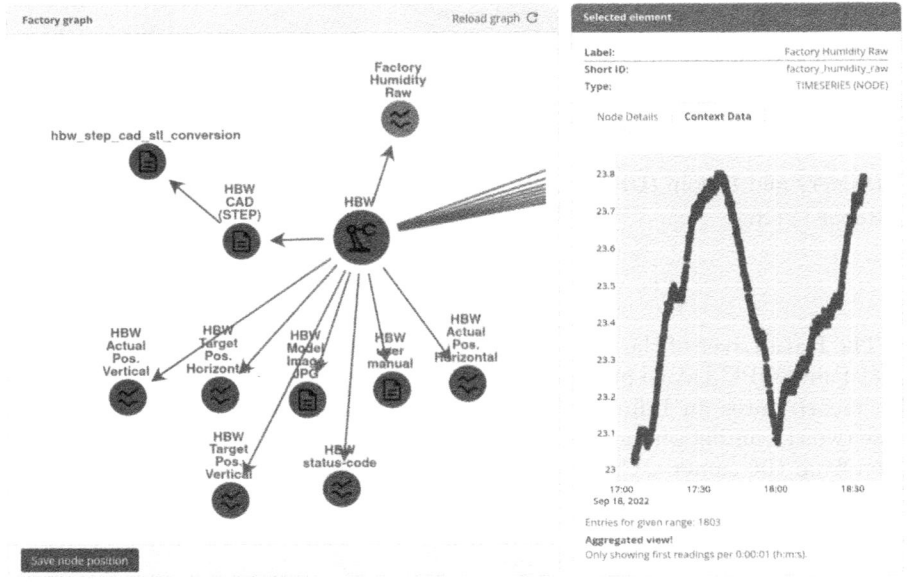

Fig. 5. Fischertechnik Factory Digital Twin Dashboard.

The Digital Twin Representation Layer also provides APIs for higher layers to retrieve data from the knowledge graph, supporting data analytics and visualization. Figure 5 shows a snapshot of the dashboard developed for the DT of the factory. A live version of this user interface is also available online[11]. The dashboard includes a window displaying the full knowledge graph and a side window visualizing the details of the selected node. As shown in Fig. 5, the historical data of the humidity value from InfluxDB is visualized in the left sidebar. Furthermore, the Service Layer of the Fischertechnik DT includes a *Similarity Pipeline* for anomaly detection in the time series data with human-in-the-loop interaction. Accordingly, the dashboard allows the user to annotate and label specific time frames of a particular time series data whenever errors occur in the factory (e.g., the sorting line gets stuck, or the NFC cannot read the data). This enables the system to learn from these annotations and improve its detection capabilities over time. By incorporating user feedback, the Similarity Pipeline can more accurately identify anomalies and provide timely alerts to prevent

---

[11] https://sindit.sintef.cloud/.

potential issues. This collaborative approach enhances the overall reliability and efficiency of the DT, making it a valuable tool for predictive maintenance and operational optimization. Details about this service can be found at [16].

4.2 Digital Twin Supporting Precision Machining

In this section, we present a pilot case for automating the deburring of large metal parts. We outline the logical blocks to be developed according to the conceptual framework of layers, and we highlight the primary benefits that SINDIT provides in supporting the user stories related to the digital twin.

This pilot aims to create a safe and responsive smart robotic solution for deburring unique and small-batch large metal parts, shifting the physical burden from humans to robots while ensuring high-quality finishes. The specific objectives include: (i) Developing a robot that collaborates with humans, navigates its environment to avoid collisions, and is easy to operate; (ii) equipping the robot with cognitive capabilities through advanced sensors and machine learning to minimize human input, enabling autonomous deburring and quality checks, and allowing the robot to learn from experience for new tasks; and (iii) ensuring the robot can autonomously and safely navigate around the parts.

The development of a series of logical components will be undertaken, detailed according to the COGNIMAN architectural framework as follows: (i) The physical layer includes device-level components such as deburring tool sensors (triaxial accelerometer, force and torque sensor, 2D Gocator laser, touch probe sensor), Automated Guided Vehicle (AGV) sensors (Ridbadge laser 2D), AGV onboard RGB and Light Detection and Ranging (LiDAR) cameras, and external sensors for detecting people and positioning parts; (ii) The data layer comprises datasets like the map and part piece model, deburring trace model, deburring feedback quality model and semantic map model; (iii) The service layer encompasses embedded software tools for navigation and deburring planning, autonomous navigation and deburring, safety awareness, semantic map generation, quality feedback and improvement, and global mission control; (iv) The digital twin layer includes the Gazebo Simulator and a real-time ROS2 board viewer; (v) The UI layer features the Human Machine Interface (HMI), and; (vi) The connectivity layer consists of software bridges for edge-cloud communication using ROS2 Data Distribution Service (DDS) and MQTT protocols.

The robotic solution, as shown in Fig. 6, consists of an AGV providing mobility for a robotic arm that performs automatic deburring functions. This system is integrated under a control system, a mobile based user interaction and a external sensor located at the ceiling of the workspace, composed by a LiDAR module and a set of mirrors that concentrate the laser beams to obtain a dense pointcloud of the space below to detect the positions of the robot and the part.

Within the pilot case, several use cases delineate the requirements of various stakeholders regarding the utilization of a DT Users aim to monitor and interact with the robotic solution via a human-machine interface, enabling tasks such as loading maps, parts, and missions, handling alerts, and adjusting priorities. They also seek the capability to perform virtual modifications to assess the robotic deburring performance prior to actual deployment. Additionally, real-time monitoring through a dashboard is desired to understand the solution's operation. For developers, particularly those working on the deburring control and semantic Simultaneous Localization and Mapping (SLAM) generator components, a virtual environment serves as an AI training ground to optimize processes and components. Furthermore, developers aim to specify technical details, including inputs, outputs, configuration parameters, and metadata such as functional descriptions, licenses, and versions, for creating or updating components. They also focus on defining, orchestrating, and parametrizing component compositions at runtime, and ensuring efficient testing and debugging of deployed solutions.

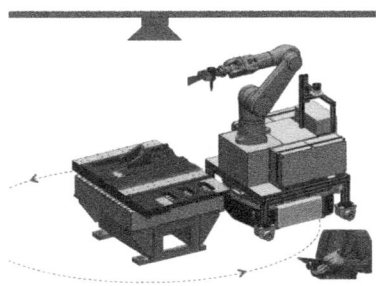

Fig. 6. Conceptual robotic approach for autonomous deburring of large metal parts.

Building upon the needs previously presented, the following lists some of the key features of SINDIT that assist in fulfilling these requirements for creating a DT in the pilot case: (i) The ability to receive information from a robot's physical sensors using various communication protocols. SINDIT includes connectors for MQTT or REST and, through its extensibility to create new plugins or components, a bridge will be integrated to directly support the DDS protocol, connecting SINDIT with a ROS2-based robot at the edge; (ii) The capability to persistently store various datasets, supporting relational, unstructured, or time-series databases. SINDIT includes components to safeguard data in various database management systems and will be able to offer a direct bridge with the COGNIMAN data cloud tool; (iii) The ability to unify and centralize the logs of distributed systems into a single data source, facilitating the monitoring and testing of the solution. SINDIT includes data safeguarding mechanisms and can establish a specific logging source that allows real-time visualization on a dashboard to facilitate debugging; (iv) The capability to include new specific services or user interface widgets for the pilot case that enable autonomous movement and deburring tasks. SINDIT allows extending its service or user interface layers through plugins or its microkernel architecture, so new components can be installed on the platform based on a standard definition and instantiated at runtime to create more complex solutions; (v) The ability to orchestrate business logic through flows that define a composition of services. SINDIT features a design environment where compositions of instantiated services on the platform can be created, along with an engine that supports their interpretation at runtime to build more complex services or automate alert generation; (vi) The capability to have a unified user interface that centralizes all layers of the solution. SINDIT provides a web-based human-machine interface and can be extended with new widgets to include real-time ROS2 dashboards and simulation environment visualizers, offering a single access point to visualize the DT from all perspectives; (vii) The ability to incorporate mechanisms for controlling user permissions and safeguarding SSH aspects. SINDIT includes a user-based authentication layer and, through new services, will encompass SSH-related aspects such as image anonymization, and; (viii) Additionally, for all those advanced functionalities that cannot or should not be integrated into the SINDIT platform itself, a REST API is provided to access each layer programmatically, thus facilitating its extension and coverage for new DT scenarios.

4.3 Digital Twin and Additive Manufacturing

Laser Powder Bed Fusion (LPBF) Additive Manufacturing (AM) processes are widely used in the medical device industry for the creation of complex components due to their high degree of design freedom. The ability of LPBF to create highly complex surfaces and geometries, including metal foams and fine lattice structures, offers great benefits for lightweighting, patient-specific implants, and osteointegration structures, giving it a significant competitive advantage over traditional manufacturing methods. Due to the complex nature of the process and the critical nature of component quality, it is essential that the process is highly qualified and that appropriate controls are put in place. In this use case, the developed framework will be applied to the LPBF process for the collection of meltpool emission data for monitoring and analysis of AM process performance. The goal of this is to develop a DT that can understand process signatures, detect anomalies and failures, and reduce overall production costs. Moreover, a DT of the process will be able to automatically analyze the process monitoring data, detect anomalies or failures, and send alerts during the printing process. It will also be capable of performing more in-depth analysis of the data to generate reports that can compare previous production runs for the same or similar components and output statistical analyses of build performance. This analysis, over time, can be compiled with physical testing and measurements to potentially reduce the quality control checks required for the process.

The 3D printer used in this use case is a Renishaw RenAM500S LPBF system, which is equipped with a single 500W laser (wavelength = 1080 nm). The focused laser spot size diameter is approximately 0.075 mm. The RenAM500S system can 3D print using both continuous and modulated laser modes. For modulated laser processing, the laser fires for a set exposure time at a given power and then switches off, subsequently moving to the next position and repeating the process. The printer's build volume is 250 mm × 250 mm × 350 mm. Example printing conditions used are: layer height: 0.030 mm, power: 200 W, point distance: 0.075 mm, and exposure time: 50 microseconds; however, these vary depending on the area of the component and the type of features to be generated. The Renishaw RenAM500S has process monitoring capabilities built into the machine, specifically the Renishaw InfiniAM Spectral system [9]. This system is equipped with three photodiode sensors that can measure the optical emissions from the laser and the meltpool. To measure the laser emissions, a fixed mirror allows a small amount of laser emission to pass through it and be detected by the LaserView module. The MeltView module has two photodiodes that measure near-infrared plasma emissions in the range of 700 nm to 1040 nm and in the near-infrared range of 1090 nm to 1700 nm. The data acquisition rate for the photodiodes is 100 kHz. The data can be post-processed into a unitless number for each photodiode that represents the emission level, with an associated X and Y coordinate. A TXT file of the raw data is generated per layer, which stores this emission data. An overview of the system is shown in Fig. 7.

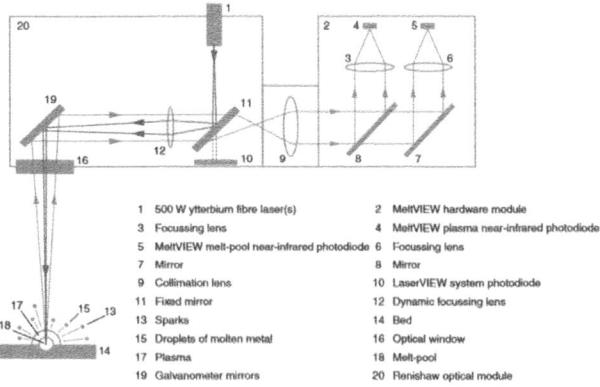

Fig. 7. Schematic of the InfiniAM Spectral system installed on the RenAM 500S LPBF 3D printer [19].

Figure 8 illustrates the overall data flow in the quality control system. The SINDIT system collects printing data from the Renishaw machine, either in batches or as a stream. This data is then preprocessed by SINDIT before being fed into the Digital Twin Model, developed by Montimage. The model evaluates the product printing quality, generating a quality report and providing alerts if any errors or defects are detected. The reports can be sent back to SINDIT for visualizing the quality results, ensuring a more efficient and accurate evaluation of the manufacturing process.

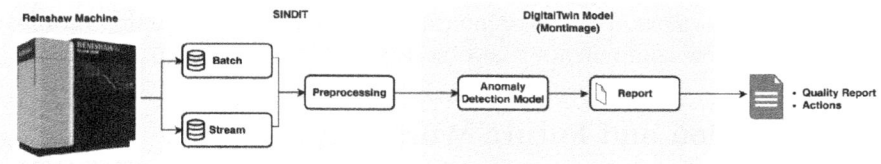

Fig. 8. Data flow of building DT for Additive Manufacturing

4.4   Discussion

The SINDIT modular architecture has demonstrated its flexibility and extensibility in advancing the field of smart manufacturing through the use of knowledge graph-based DTs. By employing a four-layer architecture, SINDIT ensures easy integration of components, facilitating the end-to-end development of DTs. This modularity allows for flexible data integration, supporting a wide variety of data sources and communication protocols. This feature is particularly beneficial in diverse manufacturing environments where different types of machinery and systems need to be interconnected.

The implementation of the DT for the Fischertechnik factory is a prime example of the capability of SINDIT. It showcases the ability of the framework to provide real-time monitoring and anomaly detection through the integration of various sensor data using MQTT and OPC-UA servers. Additionally, the knowledge graph enabled comprehensive information of the physical twins and data querying and reasoning capabilities, which are crucial for predictive maintenance and process optimization of the factory.

Moreover, the COGNIMAN project pilots in precision machining and additive manufacturing further underscore the versatility of the framework in different manufacturing settings. Although not fully implemented, the pilots highlighted the capacity of the framework to support human-machine interaction and interfacing with industrial robots, enhancing decision-making and operational efficiency. In precision machining, the framework facilitated the development of a smart robotic solution for deburring tasks, shifting the physical burden from humans to robots while ensuring high-quality finishes. In additive manufacturing, SINDIT supported the automation of post-processing meltpool emission data for analysis by the developed Digital Twin, reducing costs and improving the quality control monitoring of 3D printed medical implants.

However, several challenges and areas for improvement have been identified. One challenge is the need for advanced security mechanisms which have not been considered in the current implementation. Additionally, more components need to be developed to enhance the functionalities of the framework. For example, the Data Layer needs to be extended with more Data Connectors and Data Importers to support other databases and legacy systems, which are still being used in current industrial settings. A data analytics toolkit for the Service Layer is also required to support the dynamic development and deployment of AI/ML solutions. Furthermore, a new user interface that facilitates the configuration and integration of new components is also needed.

5   Conclusion and Future Work

The SINDIT framework has demonstrated potential in revolutionizing smart manufacturing by providing a comprehensive approach for developing knowledge graph-based DTs. The modular architecture of SINDIT, which includes flexible data integration, a generic data model, knowledge graph integration, and a service-oriented approach, ensures seamless development and deployment of DTs across various manufacturing domains. By providing unified interfaces in each layer, SINDIT facilitates the integration of external solutions for real-time monitoring, simulation, visualization and optimization of physical processes, leading to improved decision-making and operational efficiency.

The practical applications of the SINDIT framework in the COGNIMAN project, particularly in the pilots in precision machining and additive manufacturing and the Fischertechnik factory, underscore its utility and versatility, highlighting the framework's ability to drive innovation and efficiency in smart manufacturing environments.

Looking ahead, several key areas will be the focus of future developments to enhance the SINDIT framework further:

- **Integration with AAS:** Future iterations of SINDIT will incorporate AAS to provide standardized representation and interoperability of DTs, facilitating better data exchange across different platforms and systems.
- **Data Spaces Integration:** Expanding support for Data Spaces [15] will enable comprehensive data sharing, enhancing the scalability and adaptability of DTs solutions in diverse manufacturing settings.
- **Enhanced Machine Learning and Simulation Interfaces:** Developing a suite of machine learning and simulation models within the Service Layer will provide users with modular and flexible tools to customize and extend the functionalities of the SINDIT framework, improving its analytical and predictive capabilities.
- **Advanced Security Orchestration:** Implementing advanced security mechanisms, including explainable security protocols [14], will ensure the resilience and trustworthiness of DT systems against potential cyber threats.
- **Expanded Pilot Applications:** Extending the framework to more pilot projects within the COGNIMAN initiative and other industries will provide insights and validate its effectiveness in diverse manufacturing scenarios.

Acknowledgments. This work has been co-funded by the European Commission Project COGNIMAN (grant agreement No. 101058477) and the SINTEF SEP Project SINDIT 2.0. The work on the Fischertechnik factory was primarily conducted by Timo Peter during his internship at SINTEF, under the supervision of Maryna Waszak.

References

1. Amazon Web Services: Amazon TwinMaker. https://aws.amazon.com/iot-twinmaker/features/. Accessed 07 June 2024
2. Ansys: Ansys twin builder. https://www.ansys.com/products/digital-twin/ansys-twin-builder. Accessed 26 June 2024
3. Bader, S., Barnstedt, E., Bedenbender, H., Berres, B., Billmann, M., Ristin, M.: Details of the asset administration shell-part 1: the exchange of information between partners in the value chain of industrie 4.0 (version 3.0 rc02). Technical report, Federal Ministry for Economic Affairs and Climate Action (BMWK) (2022)
4. Eclipse Foundation: Eclipse ditto. https://eclipse.dev/ditto/. Accessed 26 June 2024
5. Eclipse Foundation: Eclipse vorto (2024). https://eclipse.dev/vorto/. Accessed 26 June 2024
6. Fei, T., et al.: makeTwin: a reference architecture for digital twin software platform. Chin. J. Aeronaut. **37**(1), 1–18 (2024)
7. Ghobakhloo, M.: Industry 4.0, digitization, and opportunities for sustainability. J. Clean. Prod. **252**, 119869 (2020)
8. Kamburjan, E., Klungre, V.N., Schlatte, R., Johnsen, E.B., Giese, M.: Programming and debugging with semantically lifted states. In: Verborgh, R., et al. (eds.) ESWC 2021. LNCS, vol. 12731, pp. 126–142. Springer, Cham (2021). https://doi.org/10.1007/978-3-030-77385-4_8
9. Keaveney, S., Shmeliov, A., Nicolosi, V., Dowling, D.P.: Investigation of process by-products during the selective laser melting of ti6al4v powder. Addit. Manuf. **36**, 101514 (2020). https://doi.org/10.1016/j.addma.2020.101514. https://www.sciencedirect.com/science/article/pii/S2214860420308861
10. Lam, A.N., Elvesæter, B., Martín-Recuerda, F.: Evaluation of a representative selection of SPARQL query engines using wikidata. In: European Semantic Web Conference, pp. 679–696. Springer, Cham (2023)
11. Lam, A.N., Haugen, Ø.: Implementing OPC-UA services for industrial cyber-physical systems in service-oriented architecture. In: IECON 2019-45th Annual Conference of the IEEE Industrial Electronics Society, vol. 1, pp. 5486–5492. IEEE (2019)
12. Masse, M.: REST API design rulebook: designing consistent RESTful web service interfaces. "O'Reilly Media, Inc." (2011)
13. Microsoft: Azure Digital Twins. https://learn.microsoft.com/en-us/azure/digital-twins/overview. Accessed 07 June 2024
14. Nguyen, T., Lam, A.N., Nguyen, P., Truong, L.: Security orchestration with explainability for digital twins-based smart systems. In: IEEE Annual Computer Software and Applications Conference (2024)
15. Otto, B., ten Hompel, M., Wrobel, S.: Designing Data Spaces: The Ecosystem Approach to Competitive Advantage. Springer, Cham (2022)
16. Peter, T.: Introducing cognition to digital twins through knowledge graphs and similarity measures. Master's thesis, Institut für Software & Systems Engineering, University of Augsburg, Augsburg, Germany (2022)
17. PTC: PTC ThingWorx IoT Platform. https://www.ptc.com/en/products/thingworx/. Accessed 07 June 2024
18. Quincozes, S., Emilio, T., Kazienko, J.: MQTT protocol: fundamentals, tools and future directions. IEEE Lat. Am. Trans. **17**(09), 1439–1448 (2019)

19. Renishaw: Infiniam spectral (2024). https://www.renishaw.com/resourcecentre/en/details?data=103148. Accessed 06 Aug 2024
20. Siemens: Insights hub. https://plm.sw.siemens.com/en-US/insights-hub/. Accessed 26 June 2024
21. Soori, M., Arezoo, B., Dastres, R.: Digital twin for smart manufacturing, a review. Sustain. Manuf. Serv. Econ. 100017 (2023)
22. Talasila, P., Gomes, C., Mikkelsen, P.H., Arboleda, S.G., Kamburjan, E., Larsen, P.G.: Digital twin as a service (DTAAS): a platform for digital twin developers and users. In: 2023 IEEE Smart World Congress (SWC), pp. 1–8. IEEE (2023)
23. ThingsBoard Inc.: Thingsboard. https://thingsboard.io/docs/. Accessed 07 June 2024
24. Wang, B., et al.: Human digital twin in the context of industry 5.0. Robot. Comput.-Integr. Manuf. **85**, 102626 (2024)
25. Waszak, M., Lam, A.N., Hoffmann, V., Elvesæter, B., Mogos, M.F., Roman, D.: Let the asset decide: digital twins with knowledge graphs. In: 2022 IEEE 19th International Conference on Software Architecture Companion (ICSA-C), pp. 35–39. IEEE (2022)

Enhancing IoT Security in 6G Networks: AI-Based Intrusion Detection, Penetration Testing, and Blockchain-Based Trust Management (*Work-in-Progress Paper*)

Vinh Hoa La[1](✉), Wissam Mallouli[1], Manh Dung Nguyen[1],
Edgardo Montes de Oca[1], Ana Cavalli[1], Péter Vörös[2], Károly Kecskeméti[2],
Mohammed Alshawki[2], Sándor Laki[2], Antonios Lalas[3], Sarantis Kalafatidis[3],
Asterios Mpatziakas[3], Nikolaos Makris[3], and Anastasios Drosou[3]

[1] Montimage, 39 rue Bobillot, 75013 Paris, France
vinh_hoa.la@montimage.com
[2] Faculty of Informatics, ELTE Eötvös Loránd University, 1117 Budapest, Hungary
[3] Centre for research and technology Hellas, 6th km Charilaou-Thermi Road,
57001 Thermi, Thessaloniki, Greece

Abstract. The exponential growth of Internet of Things (IoT) devices in upcoming 6G networks poses significant security challenges, particularly concerning Distributed Denial of Service (DDoS) attacks, data breaches, and unauthorized access. This paper presents the NATWORK project's approach to addressing these challenges through three distinct use cases (UC): UC#3.1 focuses on developing AI-driven machine learning techniques for anomaly detection and DDoS mitigation; UC#3.2 introduces advanced AI-powered penetration testing and vulnerability assessment tools; and UC#3.3 explores blockchain-based security mechanisms to enhance trust and secure communications in IoT ecosystems. Collectively, these use cases aim to fortify IoT networks against evolving cyber threats, ensuring data integrity and network resilience.

Keywords: IoT security · 6G networks · machine learning · DDoS attacks · blockchain · penetration testing · anomaly detection · reinforcement learning

1 Introduction

The global Internet of Things (IoT) market is projected to grow from $662.21 billion in 2023 to $3,352.97 billion by 2030[1] The large-scale deployment of IoT devices in 6G networks [8] presents substantial security challenges due to the vast number of connected devices and their inherent vulnerabilities. These devices,

---

[1] According to QuanTag IT Solutions GmbH: https://quantag-it.com/iot.html.

© IFIP International Federation for Information Processing 2025
Published by Springer Nature Switzerland AG 2025
G. Rey et al. (Eds.): IFIPIoT 2024, IFIP AICT 738, pp. 53–67, 2025.
https://doi.org/10.1007/978-3-031-82065-6_5

often with limited processing power and memory, are particularly susceptible to attacks such as distributed denial-of-service (DDoS), data breaches, and unauthorized access. To safeguard these devices and the sensitive data they handle, the network infrastructure must incorporate advanced threat detection and mitigation mechanisms.

Given that most IoT devices cannot independently support sophisticated security measures due to their resource constraints, the network itself must provide this additional layer of protection. This requires the implementation of intelligent, adaptive security solutions that can operate at scale, protecting both the devices and the data they transmit. For instance, the network could utilize AI-driven anomaly detection to identify unusual traffic patterns that may indicate a security threat. Additionally, the infrastructure could offload computationally intensive security tasks from the IoT devices to more capable network components, ensuring that even the most resource-constrained devices are adequately protected.

Moreover, privacy preservation techniques, such as end-to-end encryption and secure multi-party computation, must be integrated into the network to prevent unauthorized access to sensitive data. This approach not only secures the IoT devices but also builds a resilient and trustworthy 6G ecosystem where the security of each device is reinforced by the network's comprehensive security architecture.

The NATWORK [1] project is an innovative research initiative focused on enhancing the security, privacy, and resilience of next-generation networks, particularly within the context of the Internet of Things (IoT) and 6G ecosystems. By developing cutting-edge AI-driven security tools and methodologies, NATWORK aims to tackle the growing threats posed by cyberattacks, such as Distributed Denial of Service (DDoS) and unauthorized access, which are exacerbated by the massive scale of IoT deployments. The project brings together a consortium of leading European research institutions and industry partners to deliver robust solutions that ensure the integrity and reliability of future network infrastructures. The NATWORK project seeks to address the IoT security challenges in the context of 6G through the development of advanced security tools, leveraging AI, machine learning, and blockchain technologies.

It is important to note that this is a work-in-progress, with the NATWORK project having commenced in January 2024 and scheduled to conclude in December 2026. The ongoing research and development efforts within these use cases will continue to evolve, with the final outcomes expected to significantly enhance the security framework for IoT in 6G networks.

The rest of this paper is organized as follows: Sect. 2 provides a comprehensive review of the existing literature on IoT security challenges, with a particular focus on the emerging 6G networks and the relevant projects that have influenced our approach. Section 3 presents an in-depth discussion of the three sub-use cases explored within the NATWORK project: UC#3.1 on AI-driven anomaly detection for IoT security, UC#3.2 on AI-powered penetration testing and vulnerability assessment, and UC#3.3 on enhancing decentralized security and trust management using blockchain technology. Section 4 outlines the expected outcomes of the NATWORK project, including the key performance indicators (KPIs) aimed at improving IoT security in 6G networks. Finally, in Sect. 5, we summarize our findings, discuss the implications of our research, and propose directions for future work to further advance the field of IoT security in the context of 6G networks.

2   Background and Related Projects

2.1   Background

The deployment of Internet of Things (IoT) devices in 6G networks introduces a myriad of security challenges, primarily due to the vast number of inter-connected devices, heterogeneity, and limited computational capabilities of IoT nodes. These devices are particularly vulnerable to various cyber threats, including Distributed Denial of Service (DDoS) attacks, data breaches, unauthorized access, and routing attacks. The resource-constrained nature of IoT devices exacerbates these challenges, as they often lack the computational power to implement advanced security mechanisms. Thus, ensuring the security and privacy of IoT devices [13] and their data in 6G networks requires a robust and scalable security infrastructure.

Recent advancements in IoT security [3] have primarily focused on Intrusion Detection Systems (IDS), vulnerability assessment, and blockchain technology. AI-based IDS, particularly those employing reinforcement learning, have shown promise in adapting to dynamic IoT environments [12]. However, existing solutions often struggle with the computational constraints of IoT devices and the scalability required for 6G networks. This section reviews current IDS solutions, AI-based security mechanisms, and blockchain applications in IoT, highlighting their limitations and the need for integrated, scalable approaches.

Intrusion Detection Systems (IDS) [2] play a critical role in safeguarding IoT networks by monitoring traffic and identifying potential security breaches. Traditional IDS approaches, however, struggle to cope with the dynamic and complex nature of IoT environments. Recent advancements in Artificial Intelligence (AI), particularly machine learning and deep learning, have revolutionized IDS by enabling the development of systems that can adapt to new and evolving threats [11,16]. Reinforcement learning, for instance, has been employed to enhance IDS capabilities by allowing systems to learn from the network environment and improve detection accuracy over time. Moreover, Convolutional Neural Networks (CNNs) have shown promise in detecting anomalies in network traffic patterns, making them effective in identifying DDoS attacks and other sophisticated threats.

Penetration testing is a proactive security measure that involves simulating cyberattacks to identify and address vulnerabilities in a network. Traditional penetration testing methods are often manual and time-consuming, making them less feasible for the dynamic and expansive environments characteristic of 6G-enabled IoT networks. To overcome these limitations, AI-driven penetration testing has emerged as a promising solution. Machine learning algorithms can automate the process of vulnerability assessment by identifying potential security weaknesses and simulating various attack vectors. In the context of IoT, where the number of devices is expected to grow exponentially, automated penetration testing ensures that security measures can scale effectively. The NATWORK project, for example, focuses on developing AI-based tools for intrusion detection and penetration testing, specifically targeting the unique challenges posed by IoT devices in 6G networks.

As the number of IoT devices in 6G networks continues to grow, ensuring secure and trustworthy communication becomes increasingly challenging. Blockchain technology offers a decentralized and tamper-proof solution for managing trust in IoT networks. By leveraging distributed ledger technology, blockchain can secure communication channels between IoT devices, prevent unauthorized access, and maintain data integrity. Recent studies have explored the integration of blockchain with AI to enhance the security of IoT networks. For instance, blockchain-based access control mechanisms combined with AI-driven smart contract verification can provide robust security solutions. Additionally, reinforcement learning can be used to optimize blockchain governance, ensuring that security policies adapt to the evolving threat landscape.

2.2 Related Projects

This section provides an overview of key EU projects that members of the NATWORK consortium have been involved in, emphasizing their contributions and relevance to the initiatives discussed in this paper. These projects have laid the groundwork for the innovative approaches proposed in NATWORK, particularly in the areas of IoT security, AI-driven intrusion detection, penetration testing, and blockchain-based trust management. By building on the successes and lessons learned from these projects, NATWORK aims to further advance the security capabilities of IoT networks within the 6G framework.

SANCUS (H2020). The SANCUS project[2] focuses on the efficient and automated security of 5G Standalone (SA) networks. A key innovation of the project is the quantification of the trade-off between security, privacy, and reliability, presented for the first time through specific formulas and Key Performance Indicator (KPI) metrics.

The project leverages key tools and methodologies to enhance network security. 5Greplay [14] will be used for delivering security assessments in conjunction with the AcE engine. Additionally, the MONT Monitoring Tool (MMT) will serve as a central component for the SiD engine. In addition, CERTH contributes by bringing in expertise from AI-driven intrusion detection models developed for the SiD engine, closed-form and duality-free security optimization

---

[2] https://www.sancus-project.eu.

solutions from MiU/GiO, and AI-enhanced penetration testing modules created for the AcE engine.

SerIoT: Secure and Safe IoT (H2020). The SerIoT project[3] developed an open and reference framework designed for real-time monitoring of traffic across heterogeneous IoT platforms. The framework is capable of recognizing suspicious patterns, assessing them, and detecting security breaches, privacy threats, and abnormal events. It also provides parallel mitigation actions that operate seamlessly in the background. The project integrates software-defined networking (SDN) and Fog computing to bolster the security of IoT infrastructure.

NATWORK is leveraging security solutions developed within SerIoT. This includes the integration of monitoring and alerting solutions as well as the Service Management Plane from the Fog substrate. SerIoT also contributed to the development of machine learning-based security solutions such as anomaly detection, secure traffic routing, and cyber-attack mitigation, which will be utilized and further refined within NATWORK.

CyberSpec Armasuisse S+T. The CyberSpec project[4] focused on creating a labeled dataset to model the internal behavior of Raspberry PIs under the influence of various types of malware. This dataset captures how different malware families affect various metrics and dimensions of Raspberry PIs, which could be extrapolated to other Linux-based systems. Key metrics analyzed include Hardware Performance Counters (HPC), system calls, and resource usage (CPU, memory, and network).

Within the NATWORK project, the AI-based anomaly detection module developed in CyberSpec will be adapted to detect anomalies caused by malware. This module classifies anomalies, aiding in the selection, specification, and implementation of appropriate countermeasures. The techniques utilized in CyberSpec, encompassing both supervised and unsupervised AI-based methods, will be leveraged to enhance NATWORK's capabilities in anomaly detection and response.

3   NATWORK's Use Case 3: IoT Security

3.1   UC#3.1: Enabling Anomaly Detection Using Machine Learning Automated Techniques for Attack Detection

The growing complexity and scale of IoT networks in 6G ecosystems necessitate advanced security measures to safeguard against emerging threats, particularly Distributed Denial of Service (DDoS) attacks. UC#3.1 aims to address this challenge by developing sophisticated machine learning (ML) algorithms that can autonomously detect, classify, and respond to various DDoS attacks in real-time. This use case focuses on integrating AI-driven anomaly detection techniques to enhance the security posture of IoT networks.

---

[3] https://seriot-project.eu.
[4] https://www.csg.uzh.ch/csg/en/research/CyberSpec.html.

Machine Learning-Based Intrusion Detection. The core of UC#3.1 involves creating ML-based intrusion detection systems (IDS) capable of identifying anomalies within IoT device traffic. These anomalies often serve as early indicators of potential DDoS attacks or other malicious activities. The IDS leverages supervised learning models, particularly Convolutional Neural Networks (CNNs), which are trained on large datasets of normal network traffic. By learning the patterns of regular operations, the CNN can effectively recognize deviations that suggest the presence of an attack.

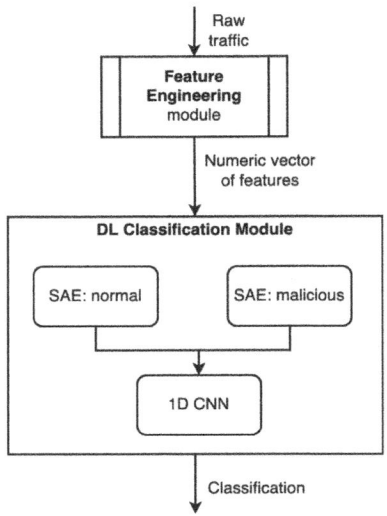

Fig. 1. Montimage AI Platform's architecture for network traffic analysis

AI-Assisted Anomaly Identification and Classification. To enhance detection accuracy, the NATWORK project integrates AI-assisted techniques for anomaly identification and classification. These advanced methods leverage sophisticated algorithms to differentiate between benign anomalies, such as network congestion, and malicious activities like DDoS attacks. The architecture of the Montimage AI Platform [9,10], as depicted in Fig. 1, forms the core of this approach. By harnessing the power of AI, the system is capable of continuous learning and adaptation, allowing it to respond effectively to new and evolving threats, thereby improving detection accuracy over time. Furthermore, the AI component supports dynamic threshold setting through reinforcement learning algorithms, which adjust the sensitivity of anomaly detection based on real-time network conditions. This adaptive approach helps to minimize false positives and enhances the overall reliability and resilience of the system.

Reinforcement Learning for Dynamic Threshold Setting. Dynamic threshold setting is crucial for maintaining a balance between sensitivity and specificity in anomaly detection. Using reinforcement learning, the system can adaptively adjust thresholds based on the real-time analysis of network traffic and historical data. This approach ensures that the IDS remains effective even as network conditions evolve, preventing attackers from exploiting static thresholds to bypass detection mechanisms.

CNNs for DDoS Attack Detection. CNNs play a pivotal role in this use case by analyzing complex network traffic patterns to detect DDoS attacks. These neural networks are particularly suited for identifying spatial and temporal patterns within the data, making them ideal for detecting sophisticated attacks that may not be apparent through traditional analysis methods. By training CNNs on a diverse set of traffic patterns, including both normal and attack scenarios, the system can accurately pinpoint when an attack is occurring and initiate appropriate mitigation measures.

Real-Time Visibility and Fast Mitigation. The combination of AI, ML, and in-network processing provides real-time visibility into the state of the network, enabling swift identification of suspicious activities. Once an anomaly is detected, the system can trigger immediate mitigation actions, such as rate limiting or traffic rerouting, to neutralize the threat. The fast reaction time afforded by these techniques is critical for protecting IoT devices and maintaining the integrity of the 6G network against DDoS attacks (Fig. 2).

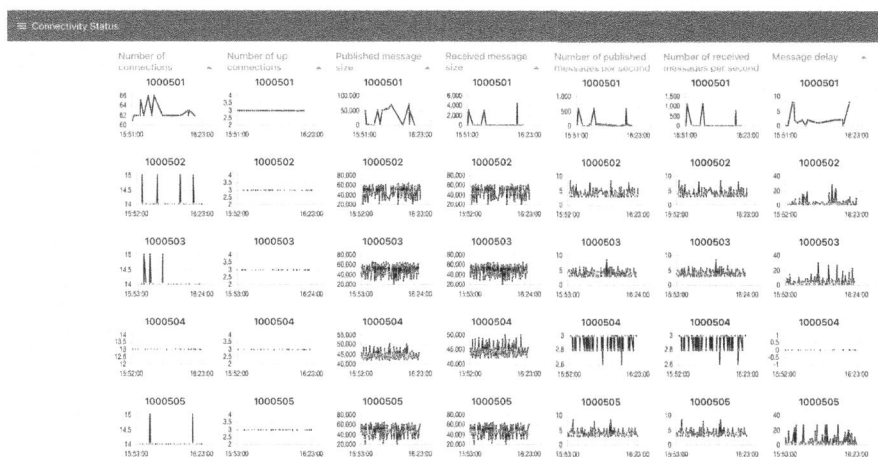

Fig. 2. Real-time visibility example provided by Montimage's Root Cause Analysis tool [7]

In-Network Acceleration and Event Detection. To meet the demands of real-time detection and response, UC#3.1 emphasizes in-network acceleration of ML models. This involves deploying lightweight ML models closer to the data source, such as at gateways or far-edge devices, to reduce latency and improve the speed of anomaly detection. Coupled with efficient data collection and event detection mechanisms, this approach ensures that the system can quickly identify and respond to threats, minimizing potential damage.

In summary, UC#3.1 represents a comprehensive approach to enhancing IoT security through automated, AI-driven anomaly detection. By leveraging advanced machine learning techniques, including Convolutional Neural Networks (CNNs) and reinforcement learning, the system can effectively detect and mitigate DDoS attacks in real-time. This use case not only bolsters the security of IoT networks but also lays the groundwork for scalable, adaptive security solutions capable of keeping pace with the rapidly evolving threat landscape in 6G environments.

3.2 UC#3.2: Validating AI-Driven Penetration Testing and Vulnerability Assessment for Attack Mitigation

As 6G networks usher in a new era of connectivity, the sheer scale and complexity of IoT deployments pose unprecedented security challenges. The vast increase in IoT devices connected to these networks demands innovative approaches to identifying and mitigating potential vulnerabilities before they can be exploited by attackers. UC#3.2 addresses this critical need by developing advanced AI-driven penetration testing and automated vulnerability assessment techniques specifically tailored for the 6G IoT landscape (Fig. 3).

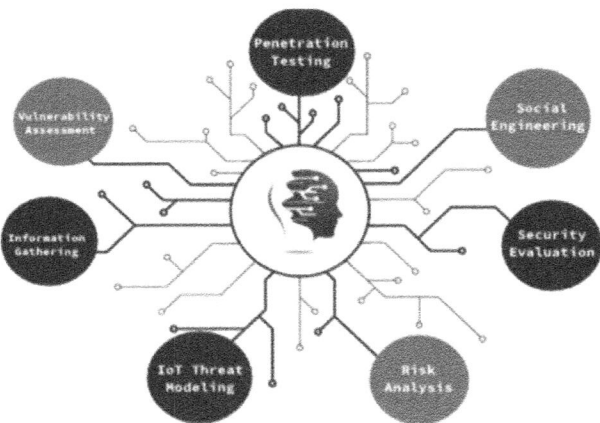

Fig. 3. Overview of AI-Driven Security Techniques in 6G IoT Networks

Machine Learning-Based Vulnerability Assessment. This feature focuses on creating automated tools that leverage machine learning to perform continuous vulnerability assessments on IoT devices. These tools will be capable of identifying potential security weaknesses and prioritizing them based on risk levels. The use of machine learning allows the system to adapt to new and emerging threats, ensuring that vulnerability assessments remain relevant and effective as the threat landscape evolves.

AI-Powered Penetration Testing. Traditional penetration testing methods are often manual and time-consuming, making them unsuitable for the dynamic and expansive 6G IoT environment. UC#3.2 aims to automate this process using AI-powered techniques, enabling rapid and thorough testing of IoT devices and networks. By simulating attacks, these AI-driven tools can identify weaknesses in a proactive manner, allowing for the implementation of countermeasures before an actual breach occurs.

Natural Language Processing (NLP) for Social Engineering Attacks. Social engineering attacks, where attackers manipulate individuals into revealing confidential information, remain a significant threat. UC#3.2 will explore the use of advanced NLP models, such as Transformers, to both understand and generate social engineering attacks. These models can analyze publicly available data, like social media profiles, to craft highly personalized and convincing phishing attempts. By understanding these tactics, the system can develop defenses to detect and prevent such attacks.

Protocol Security Analysis. Ensuring the security of communication protocols within 6G IoT networks is of critical importance. In this use case, we will conduct an in-depth analysis of the security protocols, with a particular focus on fuzzing techniques. Fuzzing will be employed to rigorously test the protocols for vulnerabilities, especially in key management processes. By injecting unexpected or malformed data into the protocol operations, we aim to uncover weaknesses that could be exploited by attackers. This approach will help in identifying potential security flaws and attack vectors, such as attack trees, that could compromise both the security and privacy of IoT networks. The results of this fuzzing-based analysis will inform the development of more robust security measures, ensuring that the protocols can withstand sophisticated cyber threats.

In short, UC#3.2 aims to provide a robust framework for preemptively securing IoT devices in 6G networks. By integrating AI-driven techniques, the use case ensures that potential vulnerabilities are identified and addressed before they can be exploited, thereby reducing the likelihood of successful attacks and minimizing service disruption. The inclusion of NLP-based social engineering detection and comprehensive protocol analysis further strengthens the security posture of IoT ecosystems. The methodologies developed in UC#3.2 will contribute to a more resilient IoT infrastructure, capable of withstanding sophisticated cyber threats. As 6G networks continue to evolve, the strategies and tools created within this use case will be instrumental in safeguarding the billions of IoT devices expected to be deployed, ensuring the continuity and security of critical services in the face of growing cyber risks.

3.3   UC#3.3: Enhancing Blockchain-Based Security and Trust Management End-to-End Security

The evolution of IoT networks within 6G ecosystems demands innovative approaches to secure communications and data processing, particularly given the decentralized nature of such environments. UC#3.3 focuses on enhancing decentralized security and trust management by leveraging cutting-edge technologies to ensure end-to-end protection across IoT devices.

Decentralized Technology for Secure Communication and Data Processing. In UC#3.3, decentralized technologies, such as blockchain [15] and distributed ledgers [6], will be employed to secure communication and data processing. These technologies offer a robust framework for ensuring the integrity and confidentiality of data, making them ideal for the highly distributed and dynamic nature of IoT networks in 6G. The decentralized approach eliminates the single points of failure that are often exploited in centralized systems, thereby enhancing the overall resilience of the network against cyber threats.

End-To-End "Lightweight" Security Mechanisms. To address the resource constraints typically associated with IoT devices, we will develop lightweight security mechanisms that provide robust protection without overburdening the devices. These mechanisms will be designed to secure all communication channels between IoT devices, ensuring that data transmitted across the network is protected from unauthorized access. The focus on lightweight solutions is crucial for maintaining the efficiency and performance of IoT devices, which are often limited in computational power and energy resources.

Decentralized Access Control and Trust Management. UC#3.3 will implement decentralized access control mechanisms to manage permissions and access rights across the IoT network [5]. These mechanisms will be complemented by trust management systems that utilize AI-powered verification and validation processes. The integration of AI in trust management will enable dynamic and context-aware decision-making, allowing the system to adapt to new threats and ensure that only authorized entities can access sensitive data or critical functions. A reference architecture is demonstrated in Fig. 4.

Formal Analysis for Protocol Security Validation. To guarantee the security and effectiveness of the proposed and adopted protocols, UC#3.3 will employ formal analysis techniques. These methods will rigorously evaluate the security properties of the protocols, identifying potential vulnerabilities and verifying

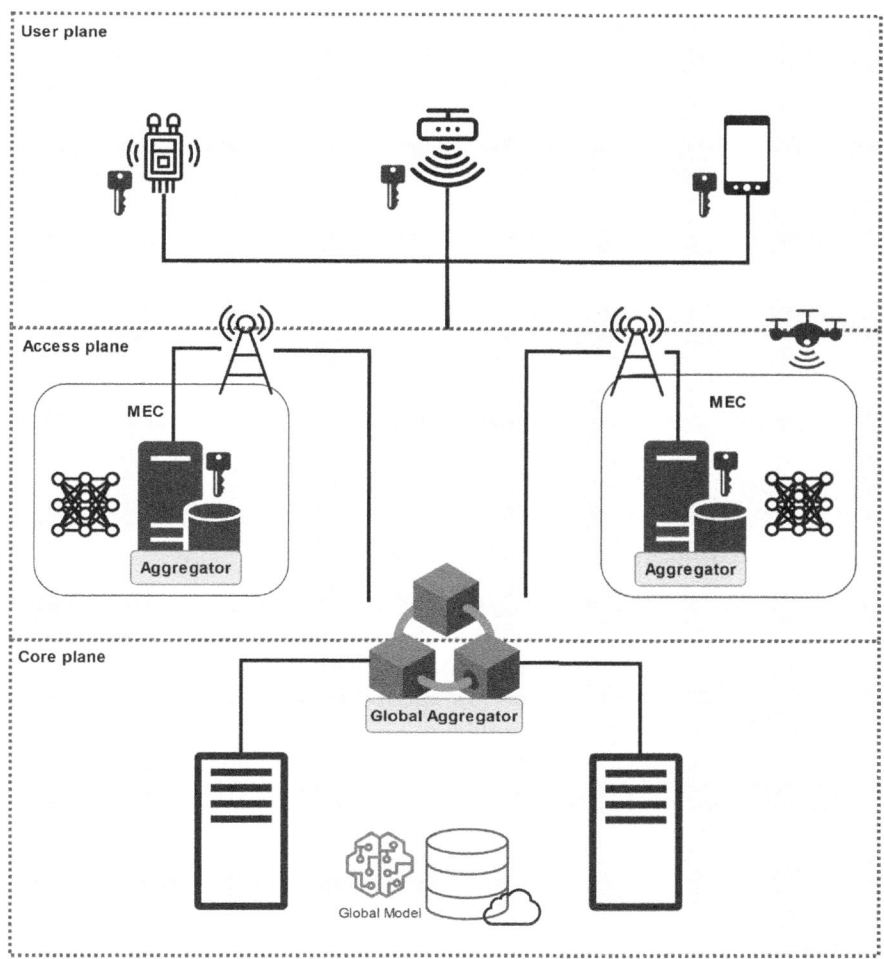

Fig. 4. Decentralized Security Architecture for IoT in 6G Networks

that the protocols meet predefined security goals. The formal analysis will serve as a critical validation step, ensuring that the decentralized security mechanisms are both theoretically sound and practically reliable.

By implementing UC#3.3, the NATWORK project aims to establish a secure and resilient IoT infrastructure for 6G networks. The decentralized security framework developed in this use case will offer a scalable solution that can adapt to the growing complexity of IoT ecosystems, ensuring that communication and data processing remain secure even as the network expands. This approach will not only protect against unauthorized access and data breaches but also build trust among network participants, fostering a more secure and reliable IoT environment.

4 Expected Outcome

To effectively assess the performance and impact of the solutions developed in the NATWORK project, specific Key Performance Indicators (KPIs) [4] have been established. These KPIs measure critical aspects of security, such as detection speed, accuracy, and system resilience. Below is a detailed description of the expected outcomes for the project's key components, aligned with the KPIs to be satisfied in the whole Use Case 3:

4.1 AI-Based Anomaly Detection and Root Cause Analysis

The AI-based anomaly detection and root cause analysis module will leverage advanced machine learning algorithms to identify and classify anomalies in IoT networks rapidly. This system is designed to detect various attack types, including Distributed Denial of Service (DDoS), data breaches, and unauthorized access, by analyzing network traffic patterns and device behaviors.

4.2 IDS and Penetration Testing Tools for IoT

The Intrusion Detection Systems (IDS) and AI-driven penetration testing tools developed for IoT networks will provide robust mechanisms for identifying vulnerabilities and preventing security breaches. These tools will be designed to operate within the constraints of IoT environments, offering high accuracy and low latency in detection and response.

4.3 Blockchain for IoT Trust Management

The blockchain-based trust management system will establish a decentralized and secure framework for managing access and ensuring the integrity of communications within IoT networks. This system will prevent unauthorized access and enhance the reliability of IoT interactions by maintaining a transparent and immutable record of all transactions.

4.4 KPI Alignment

- KPI 3.1 - Mean Time to Detect (MTTD): The solutions provided in Use Case 3 will be optimized to detect potential intrusions rapidly, with a mean detection time under 5 min for ML-based rules and 10 milliseconds for MMT rules. This quick detection is essential for preventing breaches in real-time.
- KPI 3.2 - Number of False Positives (FP): Use Case 3 tools will be fine-tuned to minimize false positives to less than 1%, ensuring that the alerts generated are relevant and accurate, preventing unnecessary interventions.
- KPI 3.3 - Number of False Negatives (FN): In Use Case 3, we aim to maintain a false negative rate of less than 1%, effectively capturing a wide range of attacks and vulnerabilities, thereby reducing the risk of undetected security breaches.

- KPI 3.4 - Packet Loss Ratio (PLR): The solutions will be optimized to handle IoT communication with minimal packet loss, ensuring a Packet Loss Ratio (PLR) of less than 0.001% even in low-bandwidth environments. This is critical for maintaining the reliability and efficiency of IoT operations.
- KPI 3.5 - Mean Time to Resolve (MTTR): The tools will facilitate rapid resolution of detected vulnerabilities or attacks, with a mean time to resolve any issues under 10 min. This quick resolution minimizes the impact of any detected threats on the IoT network's operations.
- KPI 3.6 - Encryption Coverage (EC): The architecture in Use Case 3 will ensure reaching high percentage of encryption coverage of the data both at rest and in transit.
- KPI 3.7 - Access Control Violation Rate (ACVR): The architecture in Use Case 3 aims to minimize the percentage of violation in access control which will be successful, providing a robust access control and trust based mechanism.

The expected outcomes of these three components-AI-based anomaly detection, IDS and penetration testing tools, and blockchain for trust management-are directly aligned with the project's stringent KPIs. By meeting these KPIs, NATWORK aims to significantly enhance the security and resilience of IoT networks within 6G ecosystems, addressing the evolving threat landscape with innovative, scalable solutions.

5   Conclusion

The NATWORK project's strategy for enhancing IoT security within 6G networks, as illustrated through use cases UC#3.1, UC#3.2, and UC#3.3, presents a robust and all-encompassing framework for safeguarding IoT devices against a variety of cyber threats. By incorporating advanced technologies such as AI, machine learning, and blockchain, these use cases deliver security solutions that are not only scalable and efficient but also resilient in the face of evolving challenges. Moving forward, the NATWORK project will focus on refining these approaches to enhance their efficiency and effectiveness. This will include optimizing algorithms for even faster detection and response times, reducing false positives and negatives, and ensuring that these solutions can be seamlessly integrated into larger and more complex IoT ecosystems. Additionally, the project will explore the application of these technologies to emerging IoT use cases, ensuring that the solutions remain relevant and capable of addressing the evolving threat landscape in 6G networks and beyond. By continuously improving these security frameworks, the NATWORK project aims to set a new standard for IoT security in the era of 6G.

Acknowledgement. This work has received funding from the Smart Networks and Services Joint Undertaking (SNS JU) under the European Union's Horizon Europe research and innovation programme, in the frame of the NATWORK project (Net-Zero self-adaptive activation of distributed self-resilient augmented services) under

Grant Agreement No 101139285. We would like to express our gratitude to Georgios Agrafiotis, Konstantinos Giapantzis, Virgilios Passas, Ilias Sirigos, Athanasios Korakis, Konstantinos Votis from Centre for research and technology Hellas for their invaluable contributions to the conceptualization and initial phases of this work. Although they are not listed as co-authors, their insights and efforts were crucial in shaping the direction of this research. We also acknowledge their support and collaboration throughout the course of this study.

References

1. NATWORK project. Accessed Aug 2024
2. Alotaibi, A., Barnawi, A.: IDSoft: a federated and softwarized intrusion detection framework for massive internet of things in 6G network. J. King Saud Univ. Comput. Inf. Sci. **35**(6), 101575 (2023)
3. Alotaibi, A., Barnawi, A.: Securing massive IoT in 6G: recent solutions, architectures, future directions. Internet Things **22**, 100715 (2023)
4. Chen, Y., Liu, W., Niu, Z., Feng, Z., Qiwei, H., Jiang, T.: Pervasive intelligent endogenous 6G wireless systems: prospects, theories and key technologies. Digit. Commun. Networks **6**, 312–320 (2020)
5. Fadel, M.O., Kamel, M.B.M.: Authentication and data access challenges in safeguarding industrial IoT. Lecture Notes in Electrical Engineering, vol. 1195, pp. 1–12 (2024)
6. Kamel, M.B.M., Ligeti, P., Nagy, A., Reich, C.: Distributed address table (DAT): a decentralized model for end-to-end communication in IoT. Peer-to-Peer Netw. Appl. **15**, 178–193 (2022)
7. Mallouli, W., de Oca, E.M., Nguyen, L., La, V.H.: Validation, verification and root-cause analysis. In: DevOps for Trustworthy Smart IoT Systems. Now Publishers (2021)
8. Nguyen, D.C., et al.: 6G internet of things: a comprehensive survey. IEEE Internet Things J. **9**(1), 359–383 (2022)
9. Nguyen, H.N., Nguyen, M.D., Montes de Oca, E.: A framework for in-network inference using P4. In: ARES 2024 (2024)
10. Nguyen, M.D., Bouaziz, A., Valdes, V., Rosa Cavalli, A., Mallouli, W., Montes De Oca, E.: A deep learning anomaly detection framework with explainability and robustness. In: ARES 2023 (2023)
11. Nguyen, M.-D., La, V.H., Cavalli, R., De Oca, E.M.: Towards improving explainability, resilience and performance of cybersecurity analysis of 5G/IoT networks (work-in-progress paper). In: 2022 IEEE International Conference on Software Testing, Verification and Validation Workshops (ICSTW) (2022)
12. Qadir, Z., Le, K.N., Saeed, N., Munawar, H.S.: Towards 6G internet of things: recent advances, use cases, and open challenges. ICT Exp. **9**(3), 296–312 (2023)
13. Roman, R., Zhou, J., Lopez, J.: On the features and challenges of security and privacy in distributed internet of things. Comput. Netw. **57**(10), 2266–2279 (2013). Towards a Science of Cyber Security Security and Identity Architecture for the Future Internet
14. Salazar, Z., Nguyen, H.N., Mallouli, W., Cavalli, A.R., Montes de Oca, E.: 5greplay: a 5G network traffic fuzzer - application to attack injection. In: Proceedings of the 16th International Conference on Availability, Reliability and Security, ARES 2021. Association for Computing Machinery, New York (2021)

15. Valadares, D.C.G., Perkusich, A., Martins, A.F., Kamel, M.B.M., Seline, C.: Privacy-preserving blockchain technologies. Sensors **23**(16), 7172 (2023)
16. Wang, S., et al.: Towards accountable and resilient AI-assisted networks: case studies and future challenges. In: 2024 Joint European Conference on Networks and Communications 6G Summit (EuCNC/6G Summit) (2024)

Building Digital Twins from the Unseen: Leveraging Similar Workflows to Protect IoT-Equipped Infrastructures

Bernat Coma-Puig©, Jacek Dominiak©, and Victor Muntés-Mulero(✉)©

Beawre Digital S.L., Sant Feliu de Llobregat, Spain
{bernat.coma,jacek.dominiak,victor.muntes}@beawre.com
https://www.beawre.com

Abstract. In IoT-based systems, managing risk effectively is crucial for maintaining operational continuity, especially when faced with attacks on physical assets such as sensors or actuators. These situations demand immediate and coordinated human responses to minimize damage. This paper explores the initial challenges in managing and predicting the evolution of human-involved workflows in such contexts, especially in the absence of comprehensive historical data for model training. We propose a novel approach leveraging digital twins, modeled using BPMN 2.0, to facilitate knowledge transfer across semantically similar workflows. This methodology allows for preliminary predictions regarding unmonitored workflows by utilizing insights from previously established ones. We present initial results from both synthetic and real-world data, which suggest the potential of our approach to enhance risk management practices in IoT settings. These findings are intended to foster discussion and further exploration within the research community.

1 Introduction

The rapid expansion of the Internet of Things (IoT) has dramatically transformed numerous industries by enabling seamless integration between the physical and digital worlds. This integration facilitates real-time data collection, automation, and enhanced decision-making, driving significant advancements in business efficiency and innovation [4]. However, the reliance on IoT systems also introduces new vulnerabilities, especially in critical infrastructures like healthcare, transportation, and energy sectors, where physical devices such as sensors and actuators become potential targets for disruptions.

Managing risk in IoT-dependent platforms is not merely about detecting and monitoring potential threats that compromise system integrity but also involves executing timely and effective human interventions. These interventions are critical in preventing or mitigating disruptions that could have severe consequences on public safety and service continuity. This paper addresses the significant challenges in managing and predicting the evolution of human-involved workflows in such settings, particularly in the absence of comprehensive historical data for

G. Rey et al. (Eds.): IFIPIoT 2024, IFIP AICT 738, pp. 68–86, 2025.
https://doi.org/10.1007/978-3-031-82065-6_6

model training. Traditional predictive models, which rely heavily on historical data, are often inadequate due to their inability to adapt to new or evolving workflows.

To overcome these challenges, we propose leveraging digital twins of workflows, represented through Business Process Model and Notation (BPMN) 2.0, within the framework of continuous risk management. Our method focuses on automatically identifying similar workflows and reusing trained models from these to extrapolate insights to unobserved activities in new workflows. By assuming a set of workflows expressed in BPMN, we employ machine learning (ML) models to learn from the actual execution of these workflows after monitoring them. When faced with a new workflow that lacks past data, our method facilitates the automated creation of a digital twin of the workflow, enabling reasoning and prediction based on knowledge transferred from semantically similar, previously observed workflows, thereby enhancing the capability to manage risks in IoT-equipped critical infrastructures. In this paper, we present an initial validation of our approach to find similar activities from previous workflows using both synthetic and real-world data.

The paper is organized as follows: Sect. 2 reviews related work in the field of IoT-based risk management and workflow similarity computation. Section 3 establishes the main assumption on the continuous risk management methodology, detailing the creation and application of digital twins for managing workflows. Section 4 describes our approach to creating process embeddings to enable knowledge transfer. Section 5 presents the initial results of our experiments, demonstrating the effectiveness of our approach in practical scenarios. Finally, Sect. 6 concludes the paper, discussing our findings and suggesting future research directions.

2   State of the Art

The state of the art in risk management for critical infrastructures focuses on evolving methodologies to manage the complex dynamics of these systems. Solhaug and Seehusen [10] emphasized the need for continuously updated risk models to adapt to changes, particularly in systems like air traffic management. Vuletić, Šaranović, and Vulic (2019) [11] highlighted the importance of understanding interconnected vulnerabilities and crafting appropriate protection strategies. Bialas [2] explored the application of risk management tools in critical infrastructures through the European CIRAS project, addressing interdependencies and cascading effects. Rios et al. [7] introduced the DYNABIC framework to enhance resilience through dynamic adaptation and automated responses to evolving threats. However, these studies do not specifically address the management of human-dependent workflows to mitigate high-impact disruptions in critical infrastructures.

The growing interest in automated comparison of business process models over the last decade is fueled by the availability of detailed data from repositories and the need to compare historical and current processes. Common methods include structural comparisons using graphs [6], which are quick but lack accuracy, and behavioral methods through activity profiles or execution semantics analysis [1], noted for their accuracy but complexity. Sánchez et al. [8] proposed a novel technique involving labeled tree comparisons and cophenetic distance to balance accuracy and structural analysis, yet none of these methods leverage embeddings for BPMN process similarities.

This paper introduces process embeddings, aligning with Machine Learning techniques such as Transfer Learning [13], Domain Adaptation [3], and Few-Shot Learning [12], with a unique emphasis on managing and mitigating process risks. This approach not only bridges learning methodologies but also innovates in risk management by embedding process comparisons directly.

3   Architecture of the Risk Management Framework

This section outlines the assumptions made regarding the risk management framework to provide context for the process embeddings used for knowledge transfer, as described in this paper. It is not our objective to offer insights into how AI techniques are applied within the digital twin to learn workflow evolution, nor how probabilities are set to calculate probability distributions, as these aspects are not relevant to the main purpose of this document.

Digital twins are virtual representations of physical systems that maintain a bi-directional communication with the real world. In our context, a digital twin of a workflow refers to a virtual replica of a business process, modeled using BPMN 2.0, which is continuously updated based on real-time data from multiple systems. This allows for the simulation, prediction, and management of workflow behavior, enabling proactive risk management. Unlike traditional digital twins that represent physical assets, digital twins of workflows focus on the dynamic processes involving human and automated tasks, allowing for deeper insights and predictive capabilities over process execution and risks.

Let system S be a system specifically designed to ensure effective continuous workflow risk management in critical infrastructures equipped with IoT components. The system integrates real-time data collection, prediction, and response management, comprising several key modules that play a crucial role in maintaining business continuity and mitigating risks in such environments. System S manages risks associated with business workflows involving human activities, such as maintenance tasks and operations that respond to business disruptions. By providing a comprehensive risk management framework, System S enhances the control of these workflows, ensuring that human-involved activities are executed safely and efficiently, thereby safeguarding the continuity of critical operations.

The architecture and workflow of S are detailed in Fig. 1:

1. **Data Collection Module (DCM):** The DCM continuously gathers real-time data from IoT-equipped infrastructures, including sensor readings and process logs. It also integrates information from external systems such as incident management tools and ticketing systems. This module acts as the

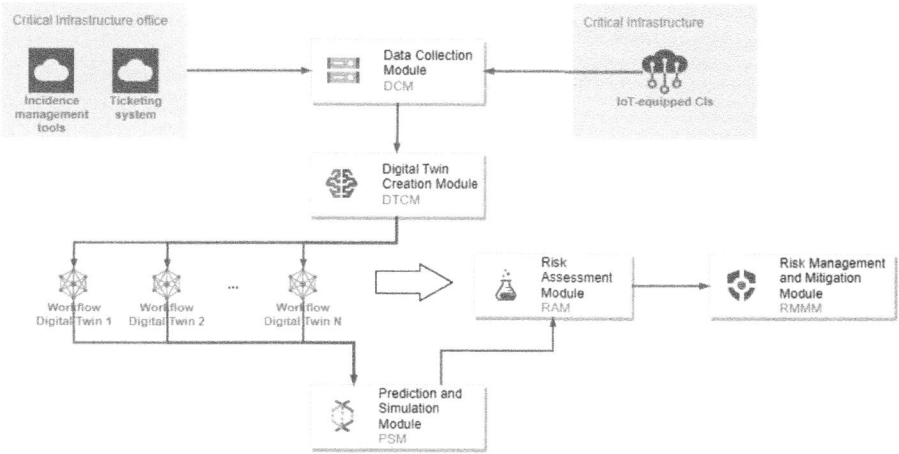

Fig. 1. Continuous risk management system to manage risks over workflows to ensure business continuity in IoT-equipped critical infrastructures.

foundational data layer for the entire system, providing critical inputs to downstream components.

2. **Digital Twin Creation Module (DTCM):** Utilizing different artificial intelligence (AI) algorithms (e.g. Gradient Boosting, LSTM, transformers), the DTCM enables the creation of digital twins crucial for predicting future executions of business processes modeled using BPMN v2.0. The DTCM systematically analyzes a representative subset of potential executions of a process, assigning specific probabilities to each feasible workflow path, through AI models that predict detailed execution specifics for individual activities within a workflow. Furthermore, the DTCM is capable of learning and predicting non-parametric distributions for critical process variables, such as the duration of workflow activities. This ability enhances the system's predictive accuracy and adaptability, enabling it to assess the risk of not meeting deadlines among other complex scenarios.

   Figure 2 illustrates a BPMN-based diagram of a digital twin, which includes machine learning models for each observable activity. This visual representation exemplifies how digital twins are structured to enable enhanced predictive capabilities within the DTCM.

3. **Prediction and Simulation Module (PSM):** The PSM leverages advanced AI algorithms to simulate future states of the workflows based on the digital twins generated by the DTCM. By anticipating potential disruptions and evaluating the impact of various scenarios, the PSM provides actionable insights into the likelihood and consequences of different events. These insights enhance preparedness and response capabilities and feed directly into the RMMM for strategic planning.

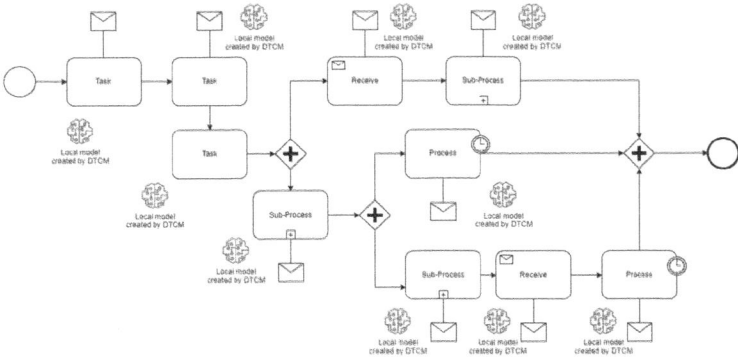

Fig. 2. BPMN-based diagram of a digital twin including ML models per activity.

4. **Risk Assessment Module (RAM):** The RAM uses PSM to analyze the digital twins and evaluates possible process executions using non-parametric distributions. It models critical variables such as process duration and assigns probabilities to different execution scenarios. By identifying potential risks, it provides crucial insights that inform the strategies for improving response processes.

5. **Risk Management and Mitigation Module (RMMM):** The RMMM coordinates and implements strategies to mitigate identified risks based on insights from the RAM. This includes proactive measures to prevent disruptions and reactive measures to manage ongoing incidents, to minimize operational impact and adapt strategies as conditions change.

4   Process Embeddings for Knowledge Transfer

In this paper, we introduce *Process Embeddings* to enable predictive capabilities for executing processes without historical data, facilitating the identification and mitigation of risks from the beginning. This method supports knowledge transfer between similar, though not identical, activities by employing principles of transfer learning. This extends machine learning beyond traditional paradigms by adapting pre-trained models to new tasks and embedding deep contextual relationships within workflows. Process embeddings incorporate textual embeddings-vector representations of text that capture semantic relationships and are used in advanced natural language processing tasks like translation and text classification. These are combined with autoencoders, neural networks that compress data into a smaller, encoded format ideal for feature extraction or dimensionality reduction. This combination allows for efficient analysis and understanding of complex language variations within process management, enhancing the predictive modeling of unseen workflows.

The high-level description of process embedding involves the following stages:

1. For a new process P without historical records, a vectorial description of each constituent activity (a_i^P) is performed. This *compression* encapsulates both textual (textual embedding) and non-textual aspects of the activity and the process as a whole. Through the autoencoder, this vectorial description is compressed into an n-dimensional vector of reduced size.
2. A repository of compressed activities from other processes is established. For each activity a_i^P, the most similar activity $a_k^{P_j}$ is identified according to a metric within the repository of processes.
3. Relevant information of the executions of $a_k^{P_j}$ is analyzed and transferred to a_i^P, effectively enriching a_i^P with historical data.
4. Predictive models for a_i^P are trained using the transferred instances of $a_k^{P_j}$.

This algorithm, therefore, allows us to train a predictive model (for instance, those described in Sect. 3) for each activity without historical data using information transferred from other similar activities.

4.1 Example of Information Processing in Processes/Activities

Each activity and process defined by our clients in our process editor includes a descriptive text explaining its function within the system. Consider P, a simple BPMN-modeled process depicting the emergency response following a cyber-attack on a power grid control system, depicted in Fig. 3.

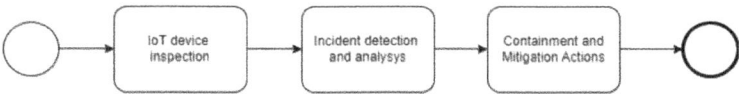

Fig. 3. BPMN process modeling the response to a cyberattack on a power grid system.

The textual description of P could be "Emergency response to a cyber-attack on the power grid, involving detection, containment, and system restoration". Each activity could be described considering its textual description, the textual descriptions of the other activities, and the overall process description. For instance, the first activity might be described as "First activity of the 'Emergency response to a cyber-attack on the power grid' process with description 'IoT device inspection'. The next activity is 'Incident Detection and Analysis'...". Through embedding, this description could be represented vectorially in an n-dimensional space, p.e., $[0.31, 0.57, -0.82, 0.15]$ in a 4-dimensional space. Furthermore, if this embedding is performed using a multilingual tool (as we have implemented in our solution), similar meanings in different languages would have a similar vector representation. Thus, two texts with similar meanings but in different languages like "Incident Detection" and "detecció d'incidents" (in Catalan) would have very similar vector representations.

Example of Non-textual Information Processing in Processes/Activities. Each activity can also be described through non-textual values. For instance, referring again to the first activity of the process depicted in Fig. 3, we might describe it (simplistically for clarity) as follows:

- Position of the activity in the sequence of executed activities to date: 1
- Total number of activities in the process: 3
- Part of a loop: 0
- Possible activities that precede this activity in an execution: 0
- Possible activities that follow this activity in an execution: 1

Thus, the process can be vectorially represented as $[1, 3, 0, 0, 1]$, a vector that includes information about the role of the activity in the process.

Activity Embedding with Textual and Non-textual Information. Once the vectorizations of textual and non-textual descriptions are obtained, it is necessary to merge them into a single embedding that represents the activity of a process in an n-dimensional space. This process embedding captures the relevant features of each input vector (see Fig. 4). Once the activity is represented in an n-dimensional space, it is possible to compare activities in this vector space to calculate similarities between them. This is typically done using cosine similarity, where the cosine of the angle formed by the two vectors indicates similarity, with 1 indicating identical vectors, 0 orthogonality, and -1 opposite vectors.

Knowledge Transfer of Activity. Once the similarity between activities is ascertainable, it becomes possible to transfer executions between similar activities $a_k^{P_j}$ (origin activity) and a_i^P (destination activity). This step requires a heuristic since it must be ensured that the variables of the origin activity's profiles have the same meaning in the destination activity. In cases where this cannot be guaranteed, the variables must be discarded. For example, consider the actual executions of $a_k^{P_j}$ described in Table 1.

Table 1. Example of activity profiles, with 4 independent variables and one dependent variable (the value to predict, duration).

ID	Activities before	Time elapsed	Avg. activity duration	Technician	Duration
Actual execution 1	4	23 h	10 h	Senior Tech.	10 h
Actual execution 2	5	30 h	9 h	Senior Tech.	15 h
Actual execution 3	3	2 h	8 h	Junior Tech.	3 h

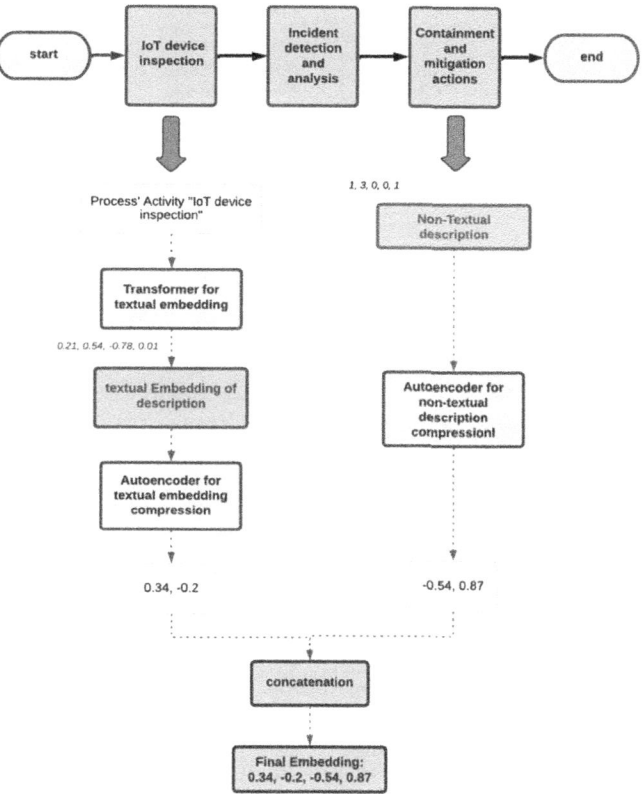

Fig. 4. Basic idea of process embedding: representing a vector considering both textual and non-textual descriptions in an embedding, which represents the activity of a process in an n-dimensional space.

The description of the variables are: (i) *activities before*: number of activities performed before in the process; (ii) *time elapsed*: time elapsed since the start of the execution; (iii) *avg. activity duration*: average duration of the activity in previous executions; (iv) *technician*: person executing the activity.

From the 4 variables that define the profile of the process's execution in the activity, 3 are model-agnostic (i.e., calculated independently of the type of process), and 1 (Technician) corresponds to information from specific process evidence. Thus, 3 variables from the executions of $a_k^{P_j}$ are reusable as useful information for a_i^P (Table 2).

In summary, if the variables that define a_i^P are "Activities before", "Time elapsed", "Average activity duration", and "Technician", we can generate a "transferred" profile using the first three variables from $a_k^{P_j}$, and assigning a "null" value to "Technician" (since there may not be equivalent in $a_k^{P_j}$).

Table 2. Transferred profiles. The variable "Technician" could not be transferred as there is no equivalent in a_i^P.

ID	Activities before	Time elapsed	Avg. activity duration	Technician	Duration
Transferred 1	4	23 h	10 h	NaN	10 h
Transferred 2	5	30 h	9 h	NaN	15 h
Transferred 3	3	2 h	8 h	NaN	3 h

Once a set of transferred knowledge is available for each activity, it is possible to train predictive models, and thus start making predictions about the execution of a process despite not having real historical executions of that same process. Once real information about new executions of the process starts to be collected, the transferred executions become less important, so a lower weight is assigned to them in the training of the models until they are eventually discarded.

5   Evaluation

The evaluation is conducted to assess the effectiveness of our techniques to find similar process activities in real-world scenarios, using real processes from large construction enterprises. This section details the methods used for the generation and comparison of processes, as well as the criteria used to evaluate the similarities between process activities.

Comprehensive Process Embedding Implementation at Beawre. In this section, we will use some of Beawre's customer processes, and we will generate new processes through generative artificial intelligence (LLM) to simulate the new processes of new customers, for whom we do not have historical information.

Below, we explain the evaluation set-up in detail:

1. The customer defines the process in Beawre's process editor in BPMN v2.0, allowing us to understand both its characteristics (such as the number of activities or the existence of parallel gateways or loops) and its textual description (process name and activity names).
2. From all processes (including the new process), we extract the possible executions from the beginning to the end of the process in order to calculate non-textual data such as for instance what is the usual position of an activity in the execution of a workflow. In our case, we limit all possible process executions to 50 activities to avoid infinite loops.
3. For each activity, a non-textual profile is created from the possible executions from the previous step and scaled between -1 and 1. Since we include variables with high ranges, and scaling helps balance the importance of each variable and also increases robustness in the training process of the AutoEncoders.

4. Additionally, for each activity, three textual descriptions are created: the description of the activity, the description of activities that can be executed before, and the description of activities that can be executed after. These descriptions are transformed using the 'paraphrase-multilingual-MiniLM-L12-v2' model. Each embedding is represented through 384 values.

5. Next, each textual embedding is compressed again. The textual description is compressed to a vector of 200 values, while the contextual textual embeddings are compressed to two vectors of 25. The difference in the size of these vectors aims to give more importance to the description of the activity and the process. In both cases, the scaling between -1 and 1 is maintained.

6. Finally, the non-textual description of the process and the three embedded textual descriptions are concatenated. At this point, we have a vector scaled to -1, 1 that includes both the textual and non-textual descriptions. The total size of the profile for each activity is 333 variables.

7. In order to make the embedding more robust, we then apply oversampling to the data by adding Gaussian noise to increase the available data (a classic technique used to improve the training process of neural networks). With these data, a GAN (Generative Adversarial Network) model is trained to generate synthetic data similar to the real ones. The GAN architecture consists of two competing neural networks: one that generates synthetic data and another that discriminates, attempting to distinguish the synthetic data.

8. We generate N synthetic data with the GAN model and train an AutoEncoder model with this dataset to reduce the data to a dimensionality of 100. With this AutoEncoder model, we can compress activities defined as the concatenation of textual and non-textual information. The AutoEncoder architecture has a complex structure, with Dropout techniques to prevent overfitting. Similar techniques are used with the GAN neural network.

9. Finally, we create a 100-dimensional embedding of all our activities. These representations can be compared using cosine similarity and implement transfer learning as explained in the previous section.

The process embedding implemented for the evaluation entails some complexity and requires some considerations:

– In this case, the embedding provides information on the activities that are executed before and after the activity is profiled. This aims to provide textual context to the profiled activity. For instance, the activity "Document Validation" can have different meanings depending on whether it is preceded by "Document Reception by the Client" or "Document Drafting by the Engineer". As we already mentioned, the dimensionality of the context information is smaller than that of the activity itself to ensure that the most relevant textual information is that of the activity and the process.

– In our original example, we separated the textual and non-textual embedding processes for the sake of descriptive simplicity. In the real implementation, by also providing information on the activities that can be executed before and after the profiled activity, there may be information that is implicitly repeated (such as the fact that more than one activity can be executed afterwards). With the combined embedding, this information is no longer repeated.

Real-World Processes Used for Evalution. Our evaluation uses three real-world processes, P_1, P_2, and P_3, from Beawre's customers in Spain and the UK, to illustrate our approach.

P_1 refers to the workflow necessary for the validation of documents by different stakeholders and it is described in detail in [5]. This is relevant in the context of IoT-related infrastructures as changes in the system may require approvals that are subject to human-generated delays, which may jeopardize a quick response in front of attacks and other events causing business disruptions.

P_2 is depicted in Fig. 5, and it refers to a process to manage document reviews before the approval. It includes activities related to the communication between the originator of a document review and the responder.

P_3 cannot be disclosed because of confidentiality issues. However, P_3 is an unrelated process, distinct from the domain of P_1 and P_2. The inclusion of P_3 serves a specific purpose: it acts as a form of "noise" in our study. P_3 challenges our approach by giving first evidence that it can differentiate between relevant and irrelevant processes. The goal is to confirm that our method is not only effective in analyzing and interpreting processes within a specific domain (P_1 and P_2) but also robust enough to exclude processes that are not related to the domain (P_3).

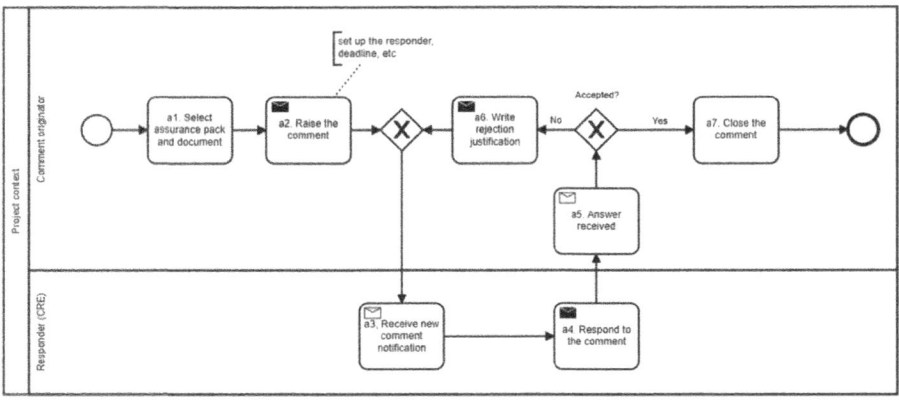

Fig. 5. Diagram of process P_2: document review management workflow.

Simulation of New Processes with Synthetic Data Generation. To evaluate the accuracy of process embedding, we simulate the addition of new processes to our platform using generative artificial intelligence to create synthetic processes based on these real-world processes, following these steps:

1. Describe to GPT-4 an original client's process model, including activities and their names, possible executions, and the overall name of the process.
2. Request GPT-4 to generate a similar process based on the described model.
3. Define the generated process in BPMN as would be done by a client and proceed with the predefined process embedding pipeline.

For the evaluation, we generate two new processes $P_{1.1}$ for P_1 and $P_{2.1}$ for P_2. Additionally, we generate a process $P_{2.2}$ for P_2 as an initial test of robustness in front of multiple languages, as all the processes are expressed in English except for $P_{2.2}$, which is written in Spanish.

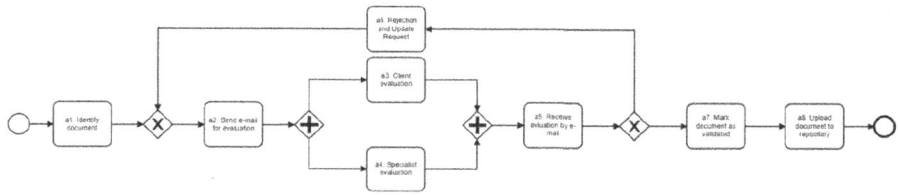

Fig. 6. Diagram of process $P_{1.1}$: document validation workflow.

In particular, $P_{1.1}$, depicted in Fig. 6, is named "Document's approval from client and specialist", representing a usual situation where some IoT-equipped infrastructure may require some changes that involve approvals from different stakeholders that may jeopardize a timely reaction in front of a business disruption. It is a process that is slightly based on P_1, although it also shares some common points (for example, in the process design) with processes P_2, which will be explained below. Its similarities with P_1 are:

– It is a process that, like in P_1, represents the evaluation and approval of a document.
– It has activities in common with P_1, such as the activities "Mark document as validated" and "Upload document to repository," which are very similar to other activities in P_1 (refer to [5]).
– It includes loops, and there are activities that are executed in parallel.

The differences are summarized below:

– It is a simpler process than P_1 in terms of the number of activities. It resembles P_2 more closely.
– The document validation process is different in $P_{1.1}$ and P_1.

Process $P_{2.1}$ is called "Issue Tracking" (see Fig. 7). We highlight the main similarities with P_2:

– Both processes represent a selection, submission, evaluation, and completion process (or iteration if the evaluation is negative).

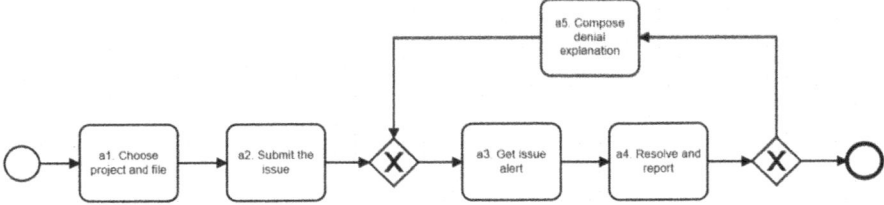

Fig. 7. Diagram of process $P_{2.1}$: issues tracking.

- They are "compact" processes with few activities.
- Both are written in English.
- They have a loop to define the iterative process of correction and validation.

The differences are summarized below:

- The original process refers to "comments", as it models the management of technical comments in meetings. In $P_{2.1}$, the process models the management of existing issues in a document.
- P_2 includes an activity after the process completion. This type of activity does not exist in this process.
- The original P_2 process represents the iteration process in a more extensive way, where the analysis and response process within the loop contains 3 activities. That said, both processes have a single "rejection" activity (in $P_{2.1}$ it would be "Compose Denial Explanation").

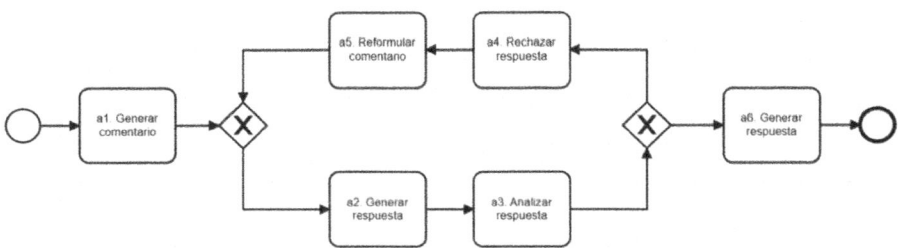

Fig. 8. Diagram of process $P_{2.2}$: evaluation of meeting comments.

$P_{2.2}$ is also derived from P_2 and is called "Evaluación de los comentarios de la reunión" (it could be translated into "Evaluation of Meeting Comments" in English from Spanish). Its similarities are summarized below (Fig. 8):

- Both models represent an iterative process where a comment on a document is generated, the comment is analyzed, and its iteration is requested, or the process is completed.

- They are compact processes with few activities.
- They have a loop.
- Both have an activity that finalizes the execution after the iteration.

Still, they have unique features that differentiate it from the original process:

- It is written in Spanish. This should not pose a problem (as we have mentioned, our solution is multilingual) but it will serve as a test for the system.
- It has two activities with the same name: "Generar respuesta" (Generate Response). This will allow us to validate the system's ability to discern the role of each activity based on contextual information (both at the textual level, including the description of activities executed before and after, as well as the non-textual profile).

Activity Comparison Evaluation. The process activities are compared using cosine similarity to determine the effectiveness of our embeddings. The outcomes are classified in Table 3.

Table 3. Classification of activities based on their cosine similarity.

Category	Description
Very Accurate	The embedding accurately identifies the activity that is contextually and functionally the most appropriate
Accurate	The identified activity is appropriate but not the optimal choice
Partially Accurate	The selected activity is acceptable but there are clearly better options
Reasonable Compromise	No optimal activity exists; the selected one is the best under the circumstances
Incorrect	The embedding fails to identify an appropriate activity

Following, as an example, we provide 3 different detailed evaluations of activities comparisons. Later on, we show the rest of the results in Table 7.

First, we look for similar activities to activity "Rejection and Update Request" (a_6 of $P_{1.1}$). The two most similar activities are described in Table 4. In this case, results are assessed as Very Accurate. Although $P_{1.1}$ was generated using Generative Artificial Intelligence based on the description of P_1, the "Rejection and Update Request" activity closely resembles a_6 of P_2, and therefore, we consider the result to be optimal.

Then, we look for similar activities to activity "Submit the issue" (a_2 of $P_{2.1}$). The two most similar activities are described in Table 5. In this case, results are assessed as Very Accurate. The option selected by the process embedding is appropriate, as it has the same function in both models: it is the preparatory activity before the iterative process of analyzing the comment/issue.

Table 4. Similarity of the "Rejection and Update Request" activity with other activities.

Description of the Variables with the Highest Similarity	Cosine Similarity
a_6 of P_2 (fourth in the loop), which indicates the rejection of the comment's response. It is the activity that causes the execution to go back, connecting with the third activity of the process.	0.7292
a_3 of P_2 (first in the loop), which indicates the receipt of the comment in the system used during the meetings, to proceed with the discussion.	0.7072

Table 5. Similarity of the "Submit the issue" activity with other activities.

Description of the Variables with the Highest Similarity	Cosine Similarity
a_2 of P_2, which consists of indicating the comment to be discussed in the meeting.	0.7769
a_1 of P_2, which consists of selecting the document on which the comment is generated.	0.6717

Finally, we look for similar activities to "Send e-mail for evaluation" ((a_2 of $P_{1.1}$)). The two most similar activities are described in Table 6. In this case results are assessed as Partially Accurate. It would be expected that the selected activity would be "Send the documentation by email" from P_1 (which had a cosine similarity of 0.6186), therefore this assignment cannot be considered very accurate. That said, the activity with the highest similarity does bear some resemblance to "Send mail for evaluation" in "contextual" terms: both are the first activity in a loop that evaluates a document, either validating or rejecting it. Therefore, its use in transfer learning would likely allow predicting the new activity with some sense, but the prediction might not be optimal.

Table 6. Similarity of the "Send mail for evaluation" activity with other activities.

Description of the Variables with the Highest Similarity	Cosine Similarity
a_3 of P_2 (first in the loop), which indicates the receipt of the comment in the system used during the meetings, to proceed with the discussion.	0.8200
a_4 of P_2 (second in the loop), which indicates that the generated comment is responded to.	0.7618

Table 7 and Fig. 9 present the evaluations of process embeddings across the test processes $P_{1.1}$, $P_{2.1}$, and $P_{2.2}$, with P_3 included as a noise factor to test the embedding's robustness and adaptability.

Table 7. Summary of Process Embedding Evaluations

Activity	Most Similar Activity	Cosine Similarity	Evaluation
a_1 of $P_{1.1}$	a_4 of P_1	0.7692	Accurate
a_2 of $P_{1.1}$	a_3 of P_2	0.8200	Partially Accurate
a_3 of $P_{1.1}$	a_5 of P_2	0.8052	Reasonable Compromise
a_4 of $P_{1.1}$	a_3 of P_2	0.7613	Reasonable Compromise
a_5 of $P_{1.1}$	a_3 of P_2	0.8150	Reasonable Compromise
a_6 of $P_{1.1}$	a_6 of P_2	0.7292	Very Accurate
a_7 of $P_{1.1}$	a_{15} of P_1	0.7560	Very Accurate
a_8 of $P_{1.1}$	a_{11} of P_1	0.7405	Very Accurate
a_1 of $P_{2.1}$	a_2 of P_2	0.6966	Accurate
a_2 of $P_{2.1}$	a_2 of P_2	0.7769	Very Accurate
a_3 of $P_{2.1}$	a_3 of P_2	0.7393	Very Accurate
a_4 of $P_{2.1}$	a_5 of P_2	0.7478	Very Accurate
a_5 of $P_{2.1}$	a_6 of P_2	0.7750	Very Accurate
a_1 of $P_{2.2}$	a_2 of P_2	0.8610	Accurate
a_2 of $P_{2.2}$	a_5 of P_2	0.8357	Very Accurate
a_3 of $P_{2.2}$	a_5 of P_2	0.8262	Very Accurate
a_4 of $P_{2.2}$	a_6 of P_2	0.8439	Very Accurate
a_5 of $P_{2.2}$	a_5 of P_2	0.8090	Partially Accurate
a_6 of $P_{2.2}$	a_7 of P_2	0.8519	Very Accurate

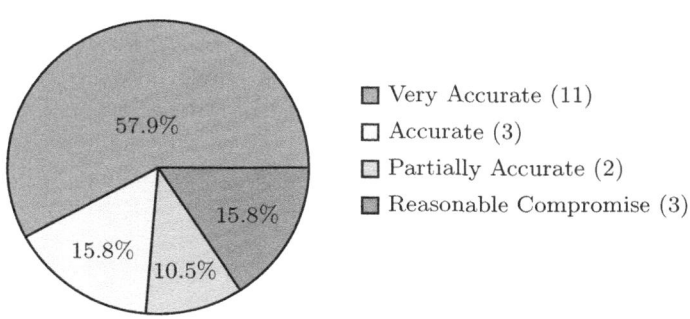

57.9%   15.8%   10.5%   15.8%

■ Very Accurate (11)
□ Accurate (3)
□ Partially Accurate (2)
■ Reasonable Compromise (3)

Fig. 9. Summary of Process Embedding Evaluations

The main conclusions drawn from these results are:

– **Robust Performance:** A majority of activities received ratings of "Very Accurate" or "Accurate," indicating that the embeddings effectively capture and match similar activities across contexts. This suggests a successful application of our embedding techniques in capturing relevant process features.

- **High Cosine Similarity Scores:** The model produced scores ranging from 0.6966 to 0.8610, demonstrating its ability to consistently recognize features that indicate activity similarities. These scores underline the model's precision in feature extraction and comparison.
- **Resilience to Noise:** The inclusion of an unrelated process, P_3, served as a noise factor to test the robustness of the embeddings. The model successfully differentiated P_3 from the domain-specific processes P_1 and P_2, indicating that it can effectively exclude irrelevant processes and focus on relevant activities. This resilience to noise is a key strength of our approach, particularly in complex environments where unrelated processes may coexist.
- **Multilingual Robustness:** The process $P_{2.2}$, expressed in Spanish, was accurately handled by the model, with cosine similarity scores comparable to those of processes expressed in English. This demonstrates the multilingual capabilities of our embedding technique, which is crucial for applications in global enterprises with processes documented in multiple languages.
- **Challenges in Handling Imperfect Matches:** The analysis reveals several instances where no direct counterparts for specific activities could be found across processes, resulting in lower cosine similarity scores than ideal. For example, activities related to iterative validation processes or evaluations by email did not have exact matches in other processes, but similar context-driven activities were identified. Despite these activities being only "Partially Accurate," they were the best matches available under the circumstances, highlighting a reasonable effectiveness in handling process variations and the intrinsic limitations of the current embeddings. This suggests areas for refinement, particularly in improving the model's ability to handle unique or non-standard activities within complex process designs.

These preliminary findings demonstrate the adaptability and potential of our process embedding techniques to improve management systems in data-scarce environments. Our methodology effectively identifies and aligns process activities with their operational needs in complex scenarios, showing resilience to noise and robustness in multilingual contexts.

6   Conclusions and Future Work

This paper presented a framework combining digital twins and process embeddings with deep learning models-Transformers and Autoencoders-to improve risk management in IoT systems. Our results demonstrate the system's ability to transfer knowledge across workflows and predict new process executions, while revealing areas for refinement, particularly in handling process-specific variables.

Though promising, this evaluation serves as a foundational step, underscoring the need for further testing across more diverse scenarios. Future work will focus on refining textual embeddings, automating hyperparameter optimization, and integrating our deep learning models into a cohesive system. We will also reassess similarity metrics and explore Large Language Models (LLMs) to enhance activity profiles and prediction accuracy.

Expanding real-world testing to include diverse datasets and industries is part of ongoing work to ensure broader applicability and robustness. Additionally, we aim to improve performance in handling activities without direct counterparts, exploring techniques like meta-learning and domain-specific adjustments.

Scalability, while not the paper's primary focus, will be addressed in future work, particularly for large-scale IoT environments with high workflow complexity. We also plan to simplify implementation for organizations with varying expertise by leveraging pre-trained models and cloud-based deployment, making the system accessible to users with limited AI experience. Future efforts will focus on developing more user-friendly interfaces and deployment models.

Acknowledgments. This research has been funded by the European Union through DYNABIC project (ID: 101070455). We acknowledge the assistance of ChatGPT-4 (OpenAI), which was used to improve readability. The content, including all scientific analyses and conclusions, was independently crafted and verified by the authors.

References

1. Armas-Cervantes, A., Baldan, P., Dumas, M., García-Bañuelos, L.: Behavioral comparison of process models based on canonically reduced event structures. In: Sadiq, S., Soffer, P., Völzer, H. (eds.) BPM 2014. LNCS, vol. 8659, pp. 267–282. Springer, Cham (2014). https://doi.org/10.1007/978-3-319-10172-9_17
2. Bialas, A.: Risk management in critical infrastructure-foundation for its sustainable work. Sustainability **8**, 240 (2016)
3. Farahani, A., Voghoei, S., Rasheed, K., Arabnia, H.R.: A brief review of domain adaptation. In: Advances in Data Science and Information Engineering: Proceedings from ICDATA 2020 and IKE 2020, pp. 877–894 (2021)
4. Lampropoulos, G., Siakas, K., Anastasiadis, T.: Internet of things in the context of industry 4.0: an overview. Int. J. Entrepreneurial Knowl. **7**, 19-4 (2019). https://doi.org/10.2478/ijek-2019-0001
5. Muntés-Mulero, V., Dominiak, J., González-Vidal, E., Rudziński, D., Ros-Batlle, X.: De-risking construction inefficiency through continuous risk management over workflows at project level. J. Arch. Des. Cons. Tech. **3**(1), 17–28 (2022)
6. Dijkman, R.M., Dumas, M., van Dongen, B.F., Käärik, R., Mendling, J.: Similarity of business process models: metrics and evaluation. Inf. Syst. **36**(2), 498–516 (2011)
7. Rios, E., et al.: The DYNABIC approach to resilience of critical infrastructures. In: Proceedings of the 18th International Conference on Availability, Reliability and Security (2023)
8. Sánchez-Charles, D., Muntés-Mulero, V., Carmona, J., Solé, M.: Process model comparison based on cophenetic distance. BPM (Forum) 141–158 (2016)
9. Sharma, A., Goyal, T., Pilli, E., Mazumdar, A., Govil, M., Joshi, R.: A secure hybrid cloud enabled architecture for internet of things. In: 2015 IEEE 2nd World Forum on Internet of Things (WF-IoT), pp. 274–279 (2015). https://doi.org/10.1109/WF-IoT.2015.7389065
10. Solhaug, B., Seehusen, F.: Model-driven risk analysis of evolving critical infrastructures. J. Ambient. Intell. Humaniz. Comput. **5**, 187–204 (2014)

11. Vuletić, D., Šaranović, J., Vulic, I.: Risk management in critical information infrastructures. In: Proceedings of the 5th IPMA SENET Project Management Conference (SENET 2019) (2019)
12. Wang, Y., Yao, Q., Kwok, J.T., Ni, L.M.: Generalizing from a few examples: a survey on few-shot learning. ACM Comput. Surv. (CSUR) **53**(3), 1–34 (2020)
13. Zhuang, F., et al.: A comprehensive survey on transfer learning. Proc. IEEE **109**, 43–76 (2019). https://doi.org/10.1109/JPROC.2020.3004555

Threats to the IoT Device Production Processes – A Blind Spot in the Product Security Lifecycle

Philipp Schubaur[(✉)][ID], Peter Knauer[ID], and Dominik Merli[ID]

THA_innos – Institute for Innovative Safety and Security, Technical University of Applied Sciences Augsburg, Augsburg, Germany
{philipp.schubaur,peter.knauer,dominik.merli}@tha.de

Abstract. The production of embedded and constrained IoT devices is a security-critical but often neglected step in the product security lifecycle. The secure development of devices has become empowered over the last decade via the implementation of DevOps processes. However, the transmission of created artifacts into the production site and onto the device itself is a regularly overlooked procedure in the security assessment. This study shows the complexity and proposes a production model that is split into four stages for analysis. The four stages comprise (1) the transmission of artifacts, (2) the management of artifacts, (3) programming of the device, and (4) provisioning of the IoT device. Assets and threat actors are defined, and critical scenarios are introduced to explain their impact on IoT device production. Concluding, the discussion presents possible approaches and their limitations based on the given variety. In the future, this will facilitate the protection of critical and valuable phases of production, thereby enhancing the security and trustworthiness of IoT devices.

Keywords: Production Security · Supply Chain Security · Manufacturing Security · DevOps · Digital Identities

1 Motivation

The Internet of Things (IoT) has become pervasive, resulting in the proliferation of interconnected devices. This trend is corroborated by recent studies that have underscored the incorporation of IoT in a multitude of applications, including smart buildings and healthcare systems [4,27,30]. In addition, the advent of modern Artificial Intelligence of Things (AIoT) approaches has gained significant traction, bolstered by the advent of dedicated hardware that handles complex tasks at the edge. AIoT enables real-time decision-making and automation by combining Artificial Intelligence (AI) algorithms with IoT data, thereby enhancing efficiency and functionality [28,36]. These devices are entrusted with the management of critical data and systems, underscoring the need for resilience. For example, smartwatches can control smart buildings, as evidenced by recent

© IFIP International Federation for Information Processing 2025
Published by Springer Nature Switzerland AG 2025
G. Rey et al. (Eds.): IFIPIoT 2024, IFIP AICT 738, pp. 87–103, 2025.
https://doi.org/10.1007/978-3-031-82065-6_7

research [3,21,35]. Another important trend of interconnected devices is the wide spread of Industrial Internet of Things (IIoT), as the components of industrial plants are interconnected [7]. This trend is expected to continue, as McKnight et al. anticipate [23].

To address the security challenges of interconnected IoT devices, software engineering efforts have placed an increased emphasis on security, resulting in the implementation of a Secure Development Lifecycle (SDL) [15]. In this context, the implementation of automation techniques that capitalize on Development and Operations (DevOps) methodologies and regular updating of devices in the field represent crucial strategies to maintain device security throughout their lifecycle. This is achieved by integrating security considerations into the development process and fostering collaboration between teams [1,22,33].

Between development using an SDL and operation of IoT devices in the field lies an overlooked but critical step: the *production phase* of IoT devices. Following the mechanical production of a device, it is essential to protect the initial deployment of firmware, generation, and enrollment of identities, as well as the activation of protective measures. It is imperative that this process is safeguarded against both external and internal threats to guarantee the integrity and security of the final product. This is in line with the report on supply chain security of IoT devices by the European Union Agency for Cybersecurity [29].

1.1   Production Procedures

The scope of the production procedures in this publication is focused on the *digital part of manufacturing* of IoT devices; specifically on the tasks associated with the injection of artifacts. In this scenario, the term *artifact* refers to an (arbitrary) combination of compiled binaries (e.g., bootloaders, kernel images, bare metal applications), file systems, bitstreams for Field Programmable Gate Arrays (FPGAs), integrated IP-cores, as well as provided identities and secrets like cryptographic key material or information for generating these as well as any other digital objects [31]. The concept and primary targets of the production process are illustrated in Fig. 1.

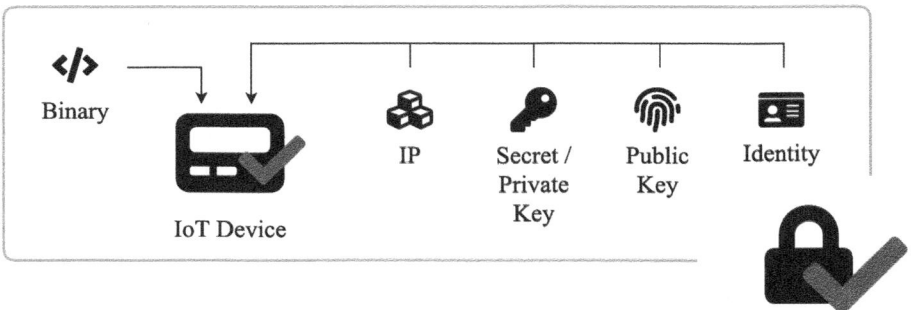

Fig. 1. Concept of IoT Device Production

After the device is mechanically manufactured, the production phase continues because the device is not equipped with any artifacts and is thus not capable of executing its desired task in the field. Therefore, it is programmed with firmware blobs, cryptographic key material, identity information, and various other Intellectual Property (IP); the latter may also be provided externally as a black or gray box. These artifacts must be applied to the device during the production phase (Fig. 1).

Secure IoT devices require individual identities and configurations. As a result, their digital production procedure is individual as well. However, applying these digital artifacts to a newly manufactured device is a complex and individual process. Yousefnezhad et al. discussed this topic in 2020, stating that the beginning of life is a crucial but complex part of the lifecycle [34].

1.2   Problem Statement

The production of IoT devices occurs at Electronics Manufacturing Services (EMSs); As a service provider, it offers Printed Circuit Board (PCB) and component procurement, as well as PCB assembly as part of the soldering process.

The most individualized nature of populating IoT devices with the requisite artifacts and identities, coupled with initial commissioning and provisioning, gives rise to a considerable degree of diversity among different products. This requires the implementation of product-specific processes.

It is therefore not feasible to secure these processes at the current status; each product requires its own individual, evaluated processes. In addition, the procedures are highly complex, intertwined, and often manually handled, introducing errors and attack vectors. Automation can streamline processes and protect against cyber threats; however, it does not inherently address the underlying complexities and challenges that persist even when processes are automated.

In addition, standards like ISO/IEC 27400 [18] and ISO/IEC 27402 [19] do not detail specific risk sources and requirements for IoT device production scenarios. Overcoming these issues, this study focuses on the following challenges:

1. How can the complex production process of an IoT device be divided into separate and assessable phases?
2. Which assets and protection goals should be considered?
3. Which threat actors and scenarios are relevant for the identified phases?

This paper contributes to the field by proposing a breakdown of complex production processes into *four distinct phases* that enable security assessments of this critical part of the product lifecycle. The associated assets and protection goals are described in each phase. By combining this information, relevant threat actors and scenarios can be proposed and discussed.

The remainder of this paper is structured as follows. Section 2 introduces the overall production phases of IoT devices. Section 3 introduces assets, protection goals, and potential attackers. This is followed by a presentation of the threat scenarios. Section 4 discusses the findings and possible mitigation approaches. Section 5 compares this to current research. Section 6 concludes the paper.

2   Stages of IoT Device Production

The transmission of artifacts for IoT devices and subsequent programming and provisioning of the devices is a multistage process. It is represented as a sequence of phases in Fig. 2.

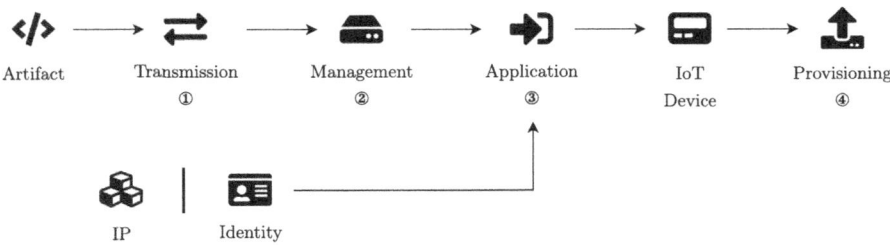

Fig. 2. Production Phases of an IoT Device

The process was divided into *four phases*, as shown in Fig. 2:

① Transmission of artifacts (data transfer)
② Management of artifacts (storage and access)
③ Application to device (programming)
④ Provisioning (activation)

These phases are characterized in the following subsections.

2.1   Transmission of Artifacts

The production of an IoT device begins with coordination work with an external EMS. After the accounting processes are completed, the EMS provider requests the assets for production.

Latter assets must be transferred from the customer to the EMS provider. For companies that operate in-house device manufacturing operations, transmission and follow-up steps are also necessary because artifacts must be transferred from development to production.

Interviews with companies have revealed significant variations in the transmission of artifacts, particularly among small and medium-sized EMS providers. It can be done in various ways; as the transport medium, it commonly relies on untrustworthy connections or exchange platforms.

The transmission ranges from unsigned and unencrypted emails, mailings with storage media, and files uploaded to external sharing platforms to limited protected storage in cloud environments. All methods have an extended number of manual interactions in common. This results in error-prone handling of artifacts and no end-to-end security.

Further, the required hashes and signatures of artifacts are computed manually on local machines. As a result, artifacts are often left unprotected across multiple computers without valid tracking.

2.2   Management of Artifacts

In the second phase, the received files are stored and managed by the EMS. As a transition from the previous step, this is also performed manually. This includes the integration of artifacts into intermediate storage.

It can be classified as an artifact *source* at an EMS site and can either be co-located to a production site, a programming station, or remote instances. This is necessary because a production batch is prepared *asynchronously* and scheduled in accordance with the available production resources at the site. Furthermore, real-time transmission of artifacts, such as identities, can be an optional requirement; however, it requires extended automation capabilities, especially the real/time capabilities of the network connection from phase ① (transmission).

Implementation may include interconnecting to an Enterprise Resource Planning (ERP) system to manage multiple orders. Modern approaches may remove this artifact management from the local site and host it at an external service, such as an arbitrary cloud computing or Version Control System (VCS) providers. The artifact source must provide the requested elements to the next phase at a given time if the production lot is triggered.

2.3   Application to Device

Artifacts are retrieved from the previously mentioned source and injected into the IoT device. To do so, this phase is divided into the following steps:

– Transfer of one or multiple artifacts
– Preparation and integration of artifacts
– Application to the device.

To be able to program artifacts onto the final IoT device, digital components must be sourced from the storage according to phase ② (storage). The transmission step also has a similar variety as phase ① (transmission), as the artifact management is usually *not* co-located to the programming station.

The production worker performs manual transfer of artifacts to external memory devices, such as USB sticks and memory cards. As a result, this procedure is error-prone, not traceable, and not scalable if a magnitude of different, device-specific files are required.

An increasing number of IoT devices are equipped with unique device certificates. This requires the generation of certificates for each device on a case-by-case basis. The manufacturing of devices is not limited to a short timeframe; it can span years; subject to market conditions, certificates are dependent on their date.

The artifact integration step may be optional because artifact individualization can be performed in various phases. The files can either be provided by the customer to each device during the phase ① (transmission) or can be altered during storage or transmission from the phase ② (storage).

Ending this production phase, the injection of integrated artifacts, identities, and arbitrary data is executed. This procedure is not evaluated retrospectively due to the progression of device production. Therefore, injection remains uneval-uated, which may result in potentially compromised or incomplete programming.

As a side effect, during product manufacturing, devices undergo quality con-trol. Therefore, explicit artifacts were used for testing. This must be erased, and the injection of the correct artifacts after testing must be evaluated and protected to ensure that all devices leave the EMS with the correct artifacts applied. The same applies to the challenges associated with reintroducing returns (e.g., from warranty cases).

Transitioning into the provisioning phase, the security features of IoT devices are initiated for the first time. This applies, e.g., to the final lock of a device by deactivating programming interfaces, enabling secure boot, and evaluating the One-Time Programmable (OTP) memory, programmed in phase ③ (program-ming).

2.4 Provisioning

Subsequently, a boot sequence of the IoT device is initiated. This procedure is specific to the final device and its application scenario. One option is registration in an operation control system, such as an intelligent building control system, as Merabet et al. presented [24].

3 Threat Analysis

Customers, primarily Small and Medium-sized Enterprises (SMEs) and EMS providers, are increasingly being faced with new cybersecurity challenges [9].

Comprehensive threat analysis constitutes the fundamental foundation of a structured cybersecurity process. Given the lack of in-depth analyses of IoT device production procedures in the current research, the following methodology was employed:

The initial step is to identify valuable assets and their associated protection goals (Sect. 3.1). Subsequently, Sect. 3.2 determines which individuals or groups might be motivated to attack those assets. Finally, relevant threat scenarios are introduced in Sect. 3.3, integrating the identified assets, protection goals, and attackers.

3.1 Assets

The production environment of IoT devices includes various assets. These assets can vary greatly depending on the nature and scope of the device. *Four* cat-egories of assets are mandatory for the production of IoT devices. This differs significantly from the deployment described by Stahl et al., which he classified as an operational practice in which release candidates that were evaluated during continuous delivery are regularly and rapidly deployed [32]. This is not sufficient in the IoT device context. Various assets are required to produce an embedded device.

Data Elements. The first type of assets, named *data elements*, aligns with familiar deployment procedures. In contrast to infrastructure or software deployment, different and proprietary file formats are required.

Artifacts Binary files, including firmware, bitstreams, and root file systems, can be employed for a range of applications in device configuration and software deployment. These formats serve as fundamental building blocks, thus enabling IoT device capabilities.

Content Text, logos, and other media files can be employed for several purposes, including the creation and dissemination of brand identity, documentation of information, and communication facilitation.

Artifact Tree An artifact tree is a tool that specifies the location of artifacts within a product. It facilitates the effective organization and mapping of different components during product development. These may also differ on a device/specific basis because the functionalities of devices are bound to specific Universally Unique Identifiers (UUIDs) [10]. The files are separate from the production management files because they are not made public to the EMS provider.

Test Firmware It is essential to test firmware and its associated artifacts in a production environment to guarantee that the final product meets the required quality standards and functions as intended before it is deployed to the customer. These firmware versions may also include dedicated functionality that is not eligible to end users.

The protection goal of confidentiality applies to artifacts and the artifact tree because the EMS provider should not be able to access the IP of the customer. However, the content may be publicly available, and the test firmware must be accessed by the EMS; thus, confidentiality is not necessarily considered. Data elements are assets according to the protection goal of integrity throughout all phases. This protection goal ensures that data and system functions remain accurate, unaltered, and trustworthy, thereby preventing unauthorized modifications and tampering. The availability of data elements is specifically required during phase ③ (programming) to enable correct injection into the device. The same applies to artifact sources during phases ① (transmission) and ② (storage), while the customer transmits data elements to the EMS provider. It is essential to verify the authenticity of assets to prevent forgery and the use of malicious artifacts. During ① (transmission), the customer must verify the EMS provider's system and vice versa before storing the transmitted data in ② (storage). In ③ (programming) and during the initial boot of the device during ④ (provisioning), the authenticity of the data elements must also be evaluated.

Identities and Cryptographic Data In addition to software and web content deployment, unique identities are central to modern and secure IoT devices. They must be generated, transmitted, and integrated into artifacts, or directly onto a device. Devices may place these identities in different locations, such as fuses, flash memory, OTP memory, or dedicated secure elements. Some IoT devices may generate them on the device itself. Thus, this category of assets must include an arbitrary combination of the following assets:

Secret/Private Keys The secret or private key is a key material commonly used in symmetric cryptography. The use of these keys serves to encrypt and decrypt data, thereby ensuring the protection of sensitive information, including commands, sensor readings, and control signals, from unauthorized access.

If asymmetric algorithms such as RSA or ECC algorithms, are used, private key material is mandatory. These keys play a decisive role in, e.g., authentication. In addition, private keys are used to encrypt short-lived symmetric keys, e.g., session keys. In some contexts, private keys may also be referred to as *secret* keys, as is the case within the OpenPGP community [13].

Public Keys. In addition to implementing private keys, the device incorporates public keys. These are essential to execute login functions, e.g., *incoming* Secure Shell (SSH) connections or server authentication.

Certificates Certificates are integrated into devices to ensure secure communication and identity verification. *Device* certificates can be used to prove a given identity, thus satisfying the requirements of modern IoT device certificates. These certificates must be uniquely generated for each device. In addition, *root* certificates can be stored on the device to verify the validity of the certificate chain. All certificates have validity periods; they must be renewed or replaced upon expiration to maintain security compliance.

Secret and private keys adhere strictly to the confidentiality principle during all phases of production. In contrast, public keys and certificates are desired for public access and are thus not affected. The integrity of key material is mandatory as well, to ensure the integrity of associated cryptographic computations. Availability is critical for the phase ③ (programming), because identities must be sourced. Customers may provide them in advance or during programming to the device. As an alternative, they may be generated by an EMS on site and transmitted to the customer, depending on the specific scenario and the customer. Depending on the generation of identities and cryptographic data, the authenticity must be verified by the customer, EMS, or a trusted third-party.

Production Management. In contrast to the deployment of web and software solutions, further information is required to manage the production of IoT devices. This includes information about part numbers and configurations, allocations of Integrated Circuits (ICs) to specific boards, UUIDs, stickers, bill of materials, information of device settings, and other highly specific information.

Serial Numbers and UUIDs The serial number of the entire device and its UUID(s) are used to uniquely identify the product. These identifiers are essential for tracking, managing, and authenticating various systems and platforms. They must be individual to any given IoT device and fixed. In addition, they can be used to track devices during the four phases of production.

IC Assignments The component assignment involves mapping individual ICs to the final IoT device. This process ensures that each part is correctly associated with the finished product to ensure proper functionality and traceability. This is particularly important if ICs are used as Root of Trusts (RoTs) or identities, e.g., a Trusted Platform Module (TPM), or a secure element.

Toolchain Configuration Information about the toolchain includes architectural design, components, access protocols, and operational workflows. These elements are critical for ensuring the appropriate handling of the devices, particularly during the phase of programming. It may consist of binaries of compilers, specific access modules for programmers, or any other data element that is necessary for a correct programming procedure.

To ensure confidentiality, access to these assets shall be limited to the customer and the EMS provider. External parties are not permitted to access production management files to prevent counterfeiting. This is in the interest of both parties to protect their IP. Elements of production management, especially the configuration of the toolchain, require integrity protection to ensure correct procedures during phase ③ (programming) and, depending on the IoT scenario, ④ (provisioning). Production management files must be available during phases ③ (programming) and ④ (provisioning) because devices may leave production without artifacts or serial numbers. If files for production management are supplied by the customer, the EMS must ensure the authenticity of toolchain procedures and IC assignments before executing them during ③ (programming) to prevent faulty devices.

Module Information. IoT devices are sometimes generic hardware platforms that differ in terms of module information. This complies with firmware parameters that provide functions for various equipment lines or parameterize sensor offsets inside a monitoring device.

Proprietary Parameters Control curves, values, and procedures, such as program sequences for dishwashers and washing machines and recipes for industrial ovens, are configured to control the device's operational behavior. It is important to ensure that these settings are correct and consistent to guarantee that the device performs the required tasks accurately and reliably in line with the desired specifications.

Confidential Features Concealed procedures can be implemented to allow secluded access to a device, such as by reactivating interfaces or accessing hidden functions and features. These backdoors are typically intended for maintenance or emergency purposes; however, they pose significant security threats if not properly managed.

IC Activation Procedures and Tokens When specialized ICs with custom-designed functionality are used, dedicated protocols are required to activate the dedicated ICs. The documentation of the required protocols ensures that the specific functionalities of the ICs are enabled and correctly incorporated into the system.

The parameters of IoT devices include IP of the customer; thus, request the protection goal of confidentiality. This may also apply to EMS providers because they are not authorized to extract this information. To maintain the desired device behavior and ensure device integrity, the parameters and IC activation should not be altered. If parameters or IC activation data are not available during phase ③ (programming), the device may either be shipped with default values or not correctly configured, resulting in inadequate device behavior. If IC activation is required, the dedicated protocols must be verified by the customer to ensure correct initialization and authentication.

3.2   Potential Attackers

Several groups or individuals motivated to attack and compromise the production of IoT devices. They can generally be divided into two groups: *external* and *internal* threat actors. The knowledge and capabilities of threat actors can vary widely.

External Threat Actors. External threat actors are groups that make no planned or necessary contribution to the production process.

> **Competitor** A competitor of the EMS or its customers may be a viable person group for attacking the production site. Colloquially, they are often referred to as "product pirates". They want to gain knowledge about IoT devices and the technology implemented to keep up with competitors' products or want to disrupt production. Latter may result in a strike against the competitor, decreasing its reliability and trustworthiness while increasing costs and inducing contract penalties.
>
> **Ransomware Group** Another external threat actor, which is driven by commercial and financial gains, is a ransomware group. Attacks against companies on their IT infrastructure are common nowadays [12,16]; ransomware shuts down all the company's working procedures. This may also be targeted at IoT device production sites, stopping or hindering EMS production because they cannot operate at full capacity.
>
> **Nation-State Attacker** The most advanced threat actor in this scenario is a nation-state attacker with nearly unlimited resources and knowledge. The primary objective may be to compromise the device in a way that does not arouse suspicion with the intention of subsequently inserting a "kill switch" to gain control of the device during its remaining operational lifespan. A nation-state attacker may also be interested in conducting a supply chain attack. This approach allows for expedient and pervasive disruption by targeting suppliers of complex and interconnected systems.

Internal Threat Actors. In contrast to external threat actors, this group of *internal* adversaries has a planned involvement in the production process. These can be separated into two groups.

Internal Employee These consist of an internal work force with varying forms of motivation and, in contrast to external threat actors, are equipped with eligible rights inside the production site of IoT devices. This is more critical because these employees are often handling artifacts according to Sect. 3.1 to initiate and monitor workflow.

Contract Worker An external contract worker is a member of the production site as part of outsourcing to an external service provider. This is common in various industries because some jobs require dedicated expertise and detailed knowledge but do not require it during all work hours.

3.3   Threat Scenarios

In the following, we describe five evident threat scenarios for the production of IoT devices backed by various assets and threat actors at a production site. This helps to communicate and understand threats, raise awareness, implement countermeasures, and improve the security of this blind spot in the product security lifecycle. If applicable, the tactics and techniques of the MITRE ATT&CK framework [25] are referenced along with their IDs.

Scenario 1: Artifacts Influenced During Transmission. A threat scenario arises if the transmission from the developer to the EMS provider during phase ① (transmission) is targeted. In the first threat scenario, a nation-state attacker can modify artifacts; specifically data elements and cryptographic data. Therefore, a surplus public SSH key can be added to the device, listed as T1090.004 in the MITRE ATT&CK framework [25]. This backdoor allows a nation-state attacker to establish a connection to an IoT device later, thereby allowing full control over the device. With this parasitic access, configuration changes can be made, or the device can be deactivated in the field. This compromises the integrity and confidentiality of the system and can lead to further security breaches. Therefore, the device can be used as an entry point for more sophisticated attacks against a customer's infrastructure. The impact of this scenario is high because total loss of data confidentiality and device control is expected.

Scenario 2: Unauthorized Access to Artifacts. The second threat scenario describes theft during phase ② (storage), the artifact management phase. This threat scenario occurs when unauthorized access is máde during storage by an external employee. Therefore, a contract worker can access the artifact source and steal module information (e.g., T1009 [25]). This may consist of, e.g., heating curves of an industrial cooking station or temperature curves of industrial kitchen appliances. He or she may release this knowledge to a competitor of the customer or to another client of the company by which he or she is originally employed. Because of this act of theft, the objective of ensuring confidentiality is undermined. The impact can be classified as moderate because the module information is typically linked to the mechanical behavior of the overall IoT device.

Scenario 3: Programming Station Suspended by an Internal Employee.
Malicious modifications to the programming of artifacts onto the device during
phase ③ (programming) is in scope of this scenario. Following a period of internal employee frustration with the company, the individual may manipulate the
programming station, resulting in system failure. This is viable because the programming station is often not encapsulated either in a mechanical or digital
manner. If this access control is not adequately implemented, it becomes impos-
sible to detect or trace any attempted manipulation. Hence, small modifications
to the production management files, specifically the toolchain information, can
create a Denial of Service (DoS) situation. This can be done via, e.g., T1072 or
T1562.001 [25]. This threat is supported by manual procedures required to control the programming station. The impact is high because the production phase
③ (programming) comes to a standstill, and no more devices can be produced
because the availability is affected.

Scenario 4: Security Features Not Activated During Programming.
If the programming station during phase ③ (programming) of the production
process is not protected, its integrity cannot be ensured. In a threat scenario, a
nation-state attacker may have network access to the production site and control the programming station. As a result, they can alter the configuration of
the latter via, e.g., T1495 [25] and hinder the activation of security features on
IoT devices. This results in devices leaving the EMS without proper activation
of security features, such as secure boot, deactivation of debug interfaces, and
secure element unlock. The impact of this is high because the protection mechanisms of the device are altered and therefore do not provide correct functionality
in the field.

Scenario 5: Stalled Identity Provisioning. During phase ④ (provisioning),
device provisioning can be impaired by a ransomware group. Individual identities and certificates are often mandatory for IoT devices. They are generated for
each device individually on an ad hoc basis. In a specific scenario, attackers may
compromise the provisioning of these identities by hijacking their source, e.g.,
an Hardware Security Module (HSM). As a result, an endpoint DoS for device
identities according to T1499 [25] can be induced; thus, provisioning fails. Without successful authentication using identities, devices cannot be entered into
the operation control system, leading to operational interruptions and economic
damage. Therefore, device availability is impaired. The impact of this scenario
is high as production stops.

4   Discussion

The threat analysis conducted on EMS providers and their customers revealed
that the IoT device production process is prone to various security threats.

Various measures must be taken to ensure production security and overcome
the shortcomings of the current state. Analysis of the decryption moment and

key material used to guarantee the confidentiality of data elements, particularly during the phase of ③ (programming).

As stated by the protection goals of identities, the generation of identities is neither clearly defined regarding time and location nor protected. In addition to managing artifacts, a reasonable solution must be considered to protect assets introduced from data elements and identities. In the case of secure elements, identities are anchored on the IoT device itself. Therefore, availability considerations are mandatory during production because these ICs require correct initialization and further interaction with external services, publishing their public key materials or certificate signing requests.

Seamless logging and monitoring as a mitigation and response option enable the rapid identification of defective IoT-devices and traceability in the event of theft, but is not used yet. In order to be able to maintain production during a DoS attack on the production site, alternative authentication paths could be viable options. These may consist of a local mirror (digital twin) of the server or IoT-Device.

These challenges must be tackled by the customer, e.g., the SMEs, by implementing secure transmission and monitoring of production procedures. Latter also needs to be encouraged by EMS providers to support generalized interfaces and empower security inside factories. The implementation of secure IoT devices is enforced by regulatory bodies, including the Radio Equipment Directive (RED) and the Network and Information Systems Directive (NIS2) [9]. In addition, the EU Cyber Resilience Act (CRA) introduces mandatory cybersecurity requirements for products with digital elements, including hardware and software, throughout their lifecycle [8]. However, the implementation of these mitigation approaches presents challenges, particularly for SMEs that lack the necessary resources and expertise.

5   Related Work

Existing literature on the security of IoT devices has highlighted several challenges, including a large attack surface, resource constraints, diverse communication protocols, and the necessity of protecting user data in compliance with privacy rules [20,26]. On the path to empower secure IoT devices, Ali and Awad [5] identified the importance of assessing security threats in IoT-based smart homes. This paper presents real-world scenarios during the usage phase of IoT devices without an in-depth analysis of the risks involved in the production. Halak describes a threat modeling approach, called "CIST" [17], however restricted to the *hardware* supply chain and detached ICs, neglecting digital artifacts. In a similar field of research, Akter et al. discussed hardware supply chain attacks [2].

The NIST guidelines strongly emphasize the importance of effectively managing the security and privacy risks inherent to this field of research. NIST SP 800-37 Rev. 2 [14] introduces a risk management framework for generic information systems, in contrast to the present publication, which focuses on the IoT production scenario. NIST IR 8228 [6] emphasizes the importance of considering security and privacy risks in a high-level IoT scenario, targeting executives without technical knowledge. Finally, NIST SP 1800-15 [11] introduces a framework for "Manufacturer Usage Description" with the objective of reducing the risk of network-based attacks.

Although these studies and regulations have provided a broad understanding of security challenges and mitigation strategies for IoT devices, they have often focused on specific aspects. In contrast, this study provides a holistic overview of security challenges in the production and provisioning phases of IoT devices.

6   Conclusion

The primary contribution of this paper is an analysis of a previously overlooked blind spot in the security lifecycle of IoT devices: the digital part of the manufacturing process.

To address the inherent security threats associated with IoT device production procedures, a comprehensive threat analysis was performed. To obtain an analyzable system, the production procedure was divided into four phases. These phases encompass the transmission of artifacts from the customer to the EMS, the storage of artifacts, the programming of artifacts onto a device, and the provisioning of the IoT device into an operating platform. The analysis involved identifying critical assets, establishing robust protection goals, delineating potential threat actors, and exploring plausible threat scenarios.

Assets were introduced and classified into four groups: data elements, identities and cryptographic data, production management, and module information. These assets can be affected by two groups of threat actors: external and internal. The external group may include nation-state attackers, competitors, and ransomware groups, whereas the internal group comprises employees.

Five threat scenarios are identified and elaborated. Namely, interference with artifacts during transmission, unauthorized access to artifacts, disruption of the programming station, failure to activate security features, and a DoS attack on identity sources.

These identified threats pose significant challenges for EMS providers and their customers, especially SMEs. Furthermore, it is important to highlight the importance of collaboration among stakeholders, including IT departments, device manufacturers, and regulatory bodies, to effectively address the security challenges inherent to the IoT device security lifecycle. IC vendors, customers, and EMS providers can develop comprehensive security strategies that cover the lifetime of an IoT device, from device manufacturing to provisioning. This is expected to result in a notable improvement in IoT security.

Acknowledgments. This study was supported by the German Federal Ministry of Education and Research (BMWK) through grant number *16KIS1956*.

References

1. Abiona, O.O., Oladapo, O.J., Modupe, O.T., Oyeniran, O.C., Adewusi, A.O., Komolafe, A.M.: The emergence and importance of DevSecOps: integrating and reviewing security practices within the DevOps pipeline. World J. Adv. Eng. Technol. Sci. **11**(2), 127–133 (2024). https://doi.org/10.30574/wjaets.2024.11.2.0093
2. Akter, S., Khalil, K., Bayoumi, M.: A survey on hardware security: current trends and challenges. IEEE Access **11**, 77543–77565 (2023). https://doi.org/10.1109/access.2023.3288696
3. Al Barazanchi, I.I., Hashim, W., Thabit, R., Sekhar, R., Shah, P., Penubadi, H.R.: Secure trust node acquisition and access control for privacy-preserving expertise trust in WBAN networks, pp. 265–275. Springer, Cham (2024). https://doi.org/10.1007/978-3-031-62881-8_22
4. Alahi, M.E.E., et al.: Integration of IoT-enabled technologies and artificial intelligence (AI) for smart city scenario: recent advancements and future trends. Sensors **23**(11), 5206 (2023). https://doi.org/10.3390/s23115206
5. Ali, B., Awad, A.I.: Cyber and physical security vulnerability assessment for IoT-based smart homes. Sensors **18**(3), 817 (2018). https://doi.org/10.3390/s18030817
6. Boeckl, K., et al.: Considerations for managing internet of things (IoT) cybersecurity and privacy risks. US Department of Commerce, National Institute of Standards and Technology (2019). https://doi.org/10.6028/nist.ir.8228
7. Boyes, H., Hallaq, B., Cunningham, J., Watson, T.: The industrial internet of things (IIoT): an analysis framework. Comput. Ind. **101**, 1–12 (2018). https://doi.org/10.1016/j.compind.2018.04.015
8. Car, P., De Luca, S.: EU Cyber Resilience Act. EPRS, European Parliament (2022). https://digital-strategy.ec.europa.eu/en/policies/cyber-resilience-act
9. Chiara, P.G.: The IoT and the new EU cybersecurity regulatory landscape. Int. Rev. Law Comput. Technol. **36**(2), 118–137 (2022). https://doi.org/10.1080/13600869.2022.2060468
10. Davis, K.R., Peabody, B., Leach, P.: Universally Unique IDentifiers (UUIDs). No. 9562 in Request for Comments, RFC Editor (2024). https://doi.org/10.17487/rfc9562. https://www.rfc-editor.org/info/rfc9562
11. Dodson, D., et al.: Securing small business and home internet of things (IoT) devices: mitigating network-based attacks using manufacturer usage description (MUD). National Institute of Standards and Technology (2021). https://doi.org/10.6028/nist.sp.1800-15
12. Everett, C.: Ransomware: to pay or not to pay? Comput. Fraud Secur. **2016**(4), 8–12 (2016). https://doi.org/10.1016/s1361-3723(16)30036-7. https://www.sciencedirect.com/science/article/pii/S1361372316300367
13. Finney, H., Donnerhacke, L., Callas, J., Thayer, R.L., Shaw, D.: OpenPGP Message Format. RFC 4880 (2007). https://doi.org/10.17487/RFC4880. https://www.rfc-editor.org/info/rfc4880
14. Force, J.T.: Risk Management Framework for Information Systems and Organizations: A System Life Cycle Approach for Security and Privacy (Discussion Draft). Technical report, National Institute of Standards and Technology (2018). https://csrc.nist.gov/pubs/sp/800/37/r2/final
15. Gokarna, M., Singh, R.: DevOps: a historical review and future works. In: 2021 International Conference on Computing, Communication, and Intelligent Systems (ICCCIS), pp. 366–371. IEEE (2021). https://doi.org/10.1109/icccis51004.2021.9397235

16. Hacquebord, F., Hilt, S., Sancho, D.: The Near And Far Future Of Ransomware Business Models. Trend Micro Research (2022). https://www.key4biz.it/wp-content/uploads/2022/12/wp-the-near-and-far-future-of-ransomware.pdf
17. Halak, B.: CIST: a threat modelling approach for hardware supply chain security. In: Halak, B. (ed.) Hardware Supply Chain Security, pp. 3–65. Springer, Cham (2021). https://doi.org/10.1007/978-3-030-62707-2_1
18. ISO Central Secretary: Cybersecurity – IoT security and privacy – Guidelines. Standard ISO/IEC 27400:2022(E), International Organization for Standardization, Geneva, CH (2022). https://www.iso.org/standard/80136.html
19. ISO Central Secretary: Cybersecurity – IoT security and privacy – Device baseline requirements. Standard ISO/IEC 27402:2023(E), International Organization for Standardization, Geneva, CH (2023). https://www.iso.org/standard/80136.html
20. Khalifa, M., Algarni, F., Ayoub Khan, M., Ullah, A., Aloufi, K.: A lightweight cryptography (LWC) framework to secure memory heap in Internet of Things. Alex. Eng. J. **60**(1), 1489–1497 (2021). https://doi.org/10.1016/j.aej.2020.11.003
21. Manogaran, G., Varatharajan, R., Lopez, D., Kumar, P.M., Sundarasekar, R., Thota, C.: A new architecture of internet of things and big data ecosystem for secured smart healthcare monitoring and alerting system. Futur. Gener. Comput. Syst. **82**, 375–387 (2018). https://doi.org/10.1016/j.future.2017.10.045
22. Mayoral-Vilches, V., García-Maestro, N., Towers, M., Gil-Uriarte, E.: DevSecOps in Robotics (2020). https://doi.org/10.48550/ARXIV.2003.10402
23. McKnight, M.: IoT, industry 4.0, industrial Iot...why connected devices are the future of design. KnE Eng. **2**(2), 197 (2017). https://doi.org/10.18502/keg.v2i2.615
24. Merabet, G.H., et al.: Intelligent building control systems for thermal comfort and energy-efficiency: a systematic review of artificial intelligence-assisted techniques. Renew. Sustain. Energy Rev. **144**, 110969 (2021). https://doi.org/10.1016/j.rser.2021.110969
25. MITRE: MITRE ATT&CK Framework (2015). https://attack.mitre.org. Accessed 05 Sept 2024
26. Nzeako, G., Okeke, C.D., Akinsanya, M.O., Popoola, O.A., Chukwurah, E.G.: Security paradigms for IoT in telecom networks: conceptual challenges and solution pathways. Eng. Sci. Technol. J. **5**(5), 1606–1626 (2024). https://doi.org/10.51594/estj.v5i5.1111
27. Parihar, V., Malik, A., Bhawna, Bhushan, B., Chaganti, R.: From smart devices to smarter systems: the evolution of artificial intelligence of things (AIoT) with characteristics, architecture, use cases and challenges, pp. 1–28. Springer, Cham (2023). https://doi.org/10.1007/978-3-031-31952-5_1
28. Pise, A.A., et al.: Enabling artificial intelligence of things (AIoT) healthcare architectures and listing security issues. Comput. Intell. Neurosci. **2022**(1), 1–14 (2022). https://doi.org/10.1155/2022/8421434
29. Skouloudi, C., Malatras, A., Naydenov, R., Dede, G.: Guidelines for Securing the Internet of Things. Technical report, European Union Agency for Cybersecurity (ENISA) (2020). https://www.enisa.europa.eu/publications/guidelines-for-securing-the-internet-of-things
30. Sleem, A., Elhenawy, I.: Survey of artificial intelligence of things for smart buildings: a closer outlook. J. Intell. Syst. Internet Things **8**(2), 63–71 (2023). https://doi.org/10.54216/jisiot.080206
31. Soares, E., Sizilio, G., Santos, J., da Costa, D.A., Kulesza, U.: The effects of continuous integration on software development: a systematic literature review. Empirical Softw. Eng. **27**(3) (2022). https://doi.org/10.1007/s10664-021-10114-1

32. Stahl, D., Martensson, T., Bosch, J.: Continuous practices and devops: beyond the buzz, what does it all mean? In: 2017 43rd Euromicro Conference on Software Engineering and Advanced Applications (SEAA). IEEE (2017). https://doi.org/10.1109/seaa.2017.8114695

33. Tatineni, S.: Compliance and audit challenges in DevOps: a security perspective. Int. Res. J. Mod. Eng. Technol. Sci. **5**(10), 1306–1316 (2023). https://doi.org/10.56726/IRJMETS45309

34. Yousefnezhad, N., Malhi, A., Främling, K.: Security in product lifecycle of IoT devices: a survey. J. Netw. Comput. Appl. **171**, 102779 (2020). https://doi.org/10.1016/j.jnca.2020.102779

35. Zakerabasali, S., Ayyoubzadeh, S.M.: Internet of things and healthcare system: a systematic review of ethical issues. Health Sci. Rep. **5**(6), e863 (2022). https://doi.org/10.1002/hsr2.863

36. Zhang, J., Tao, D.: Empowering things with intelligence: a survey of the progress, challenges, and opportunities in artificial intelligence of things. IEEE Internet Things J. **8**(10), 7789–7817 (2021). https://doi.org/10.1109/jiot.2020.3039359

STAND4IoT'24: First International Workshop on IoT Standards

Empowering Real-Time IoT Applications: A Brief Review on Leveraging GPU Acceleration for Latency Reduction

Amina Selma Haichour[1,2(✉)] and Khaled Benfriha[3,4]

[1] Ecole nationale Supérieure d'Informatique (ESI), Algiers, Algeria
a_haichour@esi.dz
[2] Laboratoire de Méthodes de Conception de Systèmes (LMCS), Algiers, Algeria
[3] Ecole Nationale Supérieure d'Arts et Métiers (ENSAM), Paris, France
khaled.benfriha@ensam.eu
[4] Laboratoire Conception de Produits et Innovation (LCPI), Paris, France

Abstract. The rapid increase in the number of IoT (Internet of Things) devices and the consequent surge in data transmission pose significant challenges to real-time data processing and telecommunication technologies. This has led to a growing interest in edge computing as a means to mitigate latency issues associated with centralized cloud processing. In this context, the integration of energy-efficient programmable GPUs (Graphics Processing Units) alongside CPUs (Central Processing Units) in IoT devices presents a promising opportunity to address latency challenges in real-time IoT applications. This brief review explores the potential of integrating energy-efficient programmable GPUs (Graphics Processing Units) alongside CPUs (Central Processing Units) in IoT devices to tackle latency issues in real-time IoT applications. The focus is on how GPUs can accelerate real-time IoT applications and minimize latency, providing valuable insights for developers looking to harness the capabilities of GPUs in IoT devices. Key considerations include identifying suitable real-time IoT applications' parts for GPU offloading and efficiently managing the offloading process.

Keywords: GPU offloading · GPU optimization · Acceleration · Latency reduction · IoT · Edge computing

1 Introduction

By connecting the physical and digital worlds, IoT devices can improve quality of life, promote social interaction and facilitate the transition to Industry 4.0 [29]. The number of IoT devices is expected to rise from 14.3 billion in 2022 to 29 billion in 2027 [45]. This rapid expansion and the massive data transmission present a noteworthy obstacle to current real-time data processing and telecommunication technologies. In fact, depending on the cloud as the main platform

© IFIP International Federation for Information Processing 2025
Published by Springer Nature Switzerland AG 2025
G. Rey et al. (Eds.): IFIPIoT 2024, IFIP AICT 738, pp. 107–120, 2025.
https://doi.org/10.1007/978-3-031-82065-6_8

for data processing can lead to increased latency due to the large data transmission over the network's limited bandwidth. This drawback can be mitigated by performing computations on the IoT device itself, inducing a rise in edge computing [20]. Scholars and experts have indeed implemented the edge-IoT paradigm to decrease latency in real-time applications. For instance, real-time and remote video analysis via IoT relies on edge computing for applications such as video surveillance, road traffic control, and smart cities [16, 44, 53].

In the context of edge computing, IoT devices' CPU faces limitations when handling compute-intensive tasks, leading to inherent latency in real-time IoT applications [25]. IoT devices now include an energy-efficient programmable GPU alongside the CPU [34]. The GPU can handle large amounts of data and perform parallel computations faster than the CPU, offering a new capability to decrease latency in real-time IoT applications. Consequently, the GPU is increasingly employed for this purpose [3, 14, 48, 49].

When utilizing the GPU to accelerate real-time IoT applications and minimize latency, the focus must be on offloading specific parts of these applications from the CPU to the GPU. These parts are difficult to identify within real-time IoT applications. Furthermore, simply offloading them to the GPU does not fully utilize its potential, as it fails to leverage the unique features of its architecture. This raises two questions that can be particularly challenging for developers engaged in building GPU executable code:

- How to identify real-time IoT applications' parts that are worth offloading to the GPU?
- How to efficiently offload the identified parts to the GPU?

This paper addresses these concerns and aims to provide valuable background for developers looking to effectively use GPUs in IoT devices for real-time IoT applications, by offering:

- Insights on identifying which parts of real-time IoT applications need to be offloaded to the GPU for acceleration.
- A thorough examination of relevant GPU architectural features and techniques that leverage them to accelerate real-time IoT applications.

The remainder of the paper is structured as follows. Section 2 summarizes IoT devices embedding a programmable GPU. Section 3 explores GPU architecture and provides a high-level overview of GPU programming. Section 4 discusses GPU offloading for accelerating real-time IoT applications, and the identification of relevant application parts for offloading. Section 5 highlights pertinent GPU architectural features and presents techniques to exploit them to accelerate real-time IoT applications. Section 6 concludes the paper.

2   IoT Devices with an Embedded Programmable GPU

IoT devices typically contain a CPU, memory components, communication peripherals, and wireless connectivity. Based on their memory and processing capabilities, IoT devices can be categorized as Low-end, Middle-end, or High-end [34]. Low-to-middle-end IoT devices have restricted memory capacity and processing power, utilizing a CPU based on an 8-bit, 16-bit or 32-bit architecture. High-end IoT devices, also known as Single Board Computers (SCBs), have significant memory capacity and a powerful multicore CPU, and may also be equipped with a GPU. Originally intended for rendering graphics, the GPU can be programmed to function as an accelerator for the CPU by executing general-purpose computations. In this type of IoT devices, the GPU is present as a Peripheral Component Interconnect express (PCIe) card, along with the host CPU [36].

The most recent high-end IoT devices with an embedded programmable GPU have been gathered and are listed in Table 1. These IoT devices come with GPUs from different vendors and can be programmed using Application Programming Interfaces (APIs), such as OpenGL, OpenCL, and CUDA [34]. OpenCL and CUDA are the most intuitive APIs and have thorough documentation, which contributes to their popularity [31]. OpenCL is vendor independent, unlike CUDA, which is a proprietary API and is only supported on NVIDIA's GPUs [19,32].

Table 1. High-end IoT Devices with an Embedded Programmable GPU.

IoT Device	GPU	Ref.
Odroid-C4	ARM Mali-G31 @600 MHz	[22]
Raspberry Pi 5	VideoCore VII @800 MHz	[37]
PINE H64	ARM Mali-T-720 @600 MHz	[38]
Jetson Nano	NVIDIA GM20B @640 MHz	[33]
Cubieboard5 Allwinner H8	PowerVR SGX544 @700 MHz	[11]
Radxa Rock Pro	ARM Mali-400 @533 MHz	[40]

3   GPU Programming

This section starts with an overview of GPU architecture, which is crucial for understanding GPU programming.

3.1   GPU Parallel Architecture

IoT devices' GPUs feature a standard architecture, comprising thousands of processing cores, memory, caches, and interconnects. This architecture is based on the Single Instruction Multiple Data (SIMD) stream, allowing cores to execute the same instruction on multiple data simultaneously [9]. The core instruction set is optimized for matrix and floating-point arithmetic, enabling the GPU to excel at linear algebra and tasks requiring a high degree of data parallelism

[46]. Additionally, the GPU is equipped with high-bandwidth memory hierarchy, facilitating rapid manipulation of large chunks of data at once [9].

The memory hierarchy on the GPU consists of global memory, similar to CPU RAM, shared memory, read-only memory, a multi-level cache system, and registers. Shared memory and read-only memory offer the developer direct control, unlike caches. Besides, shared memory has a shorter access time than global memory, while reading from read-only memory is faster than reading from a register [2,19]. These architectural features can be exploited by developers to improve GPU performance, as will be detailed in Sect. 5.

Figure 1 depicts the standard GPU architecture, with SIMD processing cores arranged in an array of core blocks. Each core block includes caches, a shared memory, and registers. The global memory and read-only memory are accessible from all core blocks.

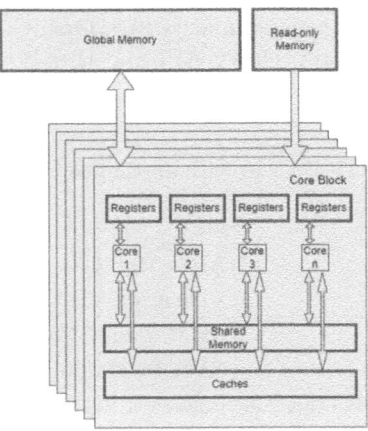

Fig. 1. Standard GPU Architecture [23].

3.2   GPU Parallel Programming

OpenCL and CUDA mentioned in Sect. 2, facilitate programming in a heterogeneous computing environment that includes the CPU (host) and the connected GPU (device). These APIs primarily offer functions for managing memory allocations on the GPU global memory, conducting CPU-GPU memory transfers, allocating shared and read-only memories, launching kernels on the GPU, and compiling these kernels to run on the GPU [19,32]. The term "kernel" denotes the part of a program's code that runs on the GPU, with a batch of threads executing it simultaneously. This execution model is called Single Instruction Multiple Threads (SIMT), combining SIMD with multithreading [52].

The threads are organized in a specific hierarchy, enabling them to be mapped to GPU resources. Indeed, a kernel is executed as a grid of thread blocks, each containing a group of threads. A thread runs on a core, and a thread block runs on a core block without the ability to migrate to other core blocks in the GPU. Figure 2 illustrates the execution of the kernel and its mapping to the available hardware resources in the GPU. All threads within a thread block can access the shared memory and synchronize with each other using barriers.

Both OpenCL and CUDA provide the launching of different kernels for concurrent execution on specific GPUs, such as those based on the NVIDIA Fermi and Pascal architectures [19]. The Jetson Nano IoT device listed in Table 1, incorporates a GPU based on NVIDIA's Maxwell architecture, which lacks this specificity.

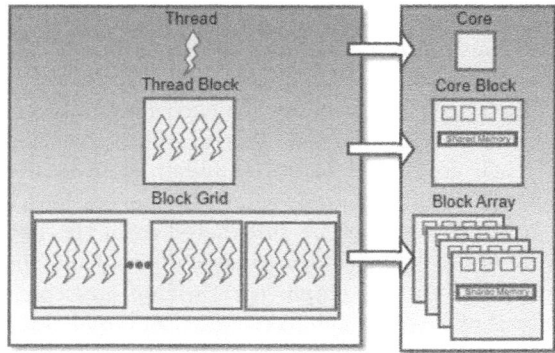

Fig. 2. Kernel Execution on GPU [19,32].

4   Accelerating Real-Time IoT Applications with GPUs

The GPU's architectural features mentioned above, such as its numerous processing cores and high-bandwidth memory hierarchy, enable it to handle extensive data and perform parallel computations faster than the CPU. Indeed, unlike the CPU, the GPU dedicates more transistors to data processing rather than to flow control [10]. Therefore, offloading parts of an application code from the CPU to the GPU offers an attractive opportunity to decrease the application response time. This approach is particularly leveraged to reduce latency in real-time IoT applications [3,14,48,49,54]. For instance, Alqarni et al. [3] reduced latency by offloading the computer vision functionality of an interactive educational game to the Raspberry Pi's GPU. When exclusively using the CPU, the game suffered from an unplayable interaction latency of 4.82 s. Offloading to the GPU decreased this to a fraction of a second, significantly improving the game's playability.

Not all real-time IoT applications' parts offloaded to the GPU reduce applications' response time and latency in the same way. Amdahl's law states that the acceleration gained by improving a single part of an application is limited by the fraction of time that the improved part is effectively used [5]. According to this law, if a part of an application, which only consumes 1% of application response time, is offloaded and accelerated by a factor 10, the application only runs 1.009 times faster. Conversely, if it consumes 75% of the time and is offloaded and accelerated by a factor 10, the application runs 3.07 times faster. In fact, Alqarni et al. offloaded the computer vision functionality as it is time-consuming. Similarly, Stylianopoulos et al. [49] offloaded the pattern matching functionality in the proposed IoT intrusion detection system. To notably reduce real-time IoT applications' response time and latency, the focus must be on offloading time-consuming parts from the CPU to the GPU. Offloading non-time-consuming parts is not beneficial as it only increases the cost of CPU-GPU memory transfers, which negatively impacts real-time IoT applications' response time and latency.

Identifying time-consuming parts, also known as hotspot functions, is crucial for efficiently accelerating real-time IoT applications and is the initial step before any GPU offloading. This can be achieved manually in a real-time IoT application code by employing routines to track the execution time of different functions and their frequency of use (number of invocations). Additional routines to extract the result for analysis are also necessary. The overhead of running all these routines needs to be subtracted from the final result. Hence, manually identifying hotspot functions increases design time and costs. To overcome this issue, profilers can be employed. Profilers are tools that allow the collection and analysis of execution characteristics of a real-time IoT application code. They provide interactive graphics that developers can easily assess. There are various profilers designed for specific programming languages and operating systems [4,6,26]. Their analysis results may vary, so combining different results can be beneficial for a more comprehensive assessment [15].

Once hotspot functions are identified, they can be offloaded to the GPU by transforming them into kernels that utilize parallelism and transferring the required data for computations. Accelerating a real-time IoT application using a GPU is achievable through this process, which can be done using function calls provided by the aforementioned APIs. This process can be further enhanced for improved acceleration by optimizing GPU performance which will be discussed in Sect. 5.

5   Optimizing GPU Performance to Accelerate Real-Time IoT Applications

Developers can significantly improve real-time IoT application acceleration by leveraging the specific architectural features of GPUs through optimizations. These optimizations are considered low-level because they enhance aspects dependent on the hardware architecture on which the code runs [7]. Hijma et al. [23] demonstrated the importance of optimizations on the performance of NVIDIA GPUs. They tested GPU offloading without optimizations, and then with optimizations for several hotspot functions of well-known problems. Their results revealed that accelerations obtained with optimizations can double or even increase by 8 times compared to accelerations obtained without optimizations.

This section examines the key GPU performance optimizations by categorizing them into optimizations that aim to maximize GPU parallel execution and those that aim to reduce GPU memory access latency.

5.1   Maximizing GPU Parallel Execution

– **Organizing Threads.** GPU offloading involves converting a part of an application into a kernel and initiating it with a specified number of threads to utilize GPU inherent parallelism, as determined by the developer. For example, when a developer aims to parallelize a 1024-vector addition, the kernel is initiated with the number of threads adjusted to match the vector dimension (1024). OpenCL and CUDA enable the developer, when initiating the kernel, to arrange the specified number of threads into multiple thread blocks [19,32]. If the developer neglects this functionality and arranges the threads as a single thread block, there is a risk of compromising GPU performance. This is due to the the limited number of threads that can be simultaneously executed on a single core block [23]. Assuming this limit is 16 threads, the 1024 threads from the previous example cannot all be executed simultaneously. They are divided into 64 groups of 16 threads, to be serially executed on the core block. To maximize thread-level parallelism, it is necessary to arrange them into multiple thread blocks, forming a grid of thread blocks as shown in Fig. 2, that can be executed simultaneously on distinct core blocks. In the example, the kernel should be initiated with 1024 threads arranged as 64 thread blocks of 16 threads, which run simultaneously on 64 core blocks. Running multiple threads arranged into multiple thread blocks is considered a fundamental optimization for maximizing GPU parallel execution and is widely used [17,49].
– **Minimizing Divergent Threads.** When threads on a single core block execute a conditional instruction, they may take different paths and execute different instructions next. This behaviour contrasts with the GPU's SIMT execution model, which forces serialized thread execution on a single core block, significantly impacting GPU performance [51]. Kernel fission is employed to mitigate divergent threads by splitting a single kernel into multiple small kernels [12,21]. It facilitates the grouping of threads with similar execution paths into the same kernel, enabling their parallel execution on each allocated core block. Hijma et al. [23] utilized this optimization and achieved a 17% increase in application acceleration. Figure 3 shows a straightforward illustration of kernel fission, with the kernel in (1) being split into two kernels in (2).
– **Enabling Concurrent Kernels.** By default, OpenCL and CUDA run one kernel at a time on the GPU when launching multiple kernels as in kernel fission [19,32]. The two APIs provide the developer function calls to unlock the GPU to start another kernel before the current one finishes, thereby

enhancing thread-level parallelism through concurrent kernel execution. This could be even more interesting with a multicore CPU permitting simultaneous launching of CPU threads to execute kernels [41]. Indeed, prior research highlighted GPU performance improvements resulting from the concurrent execution of kernels [13,52]. Nonetheless, as indicated in Subsect. 3.2, this capability is not universally supported across all GPUs.

```
1  int main() {
2      ...
3      int a = 5;
4      /*run work() kernel*/
5      ...
6  }
7  kernel void work(int a){
8      if(a){
9          /*do work 1*/
10      }else{
11          /*do work 2*/
12      }
13 }
```

(1)

```
1  int main() {
2      ...
3      int a = 5;
4      if(a){
5          /*run work1() kernel*/
6      }else{
7          /*run work2() kernel*/
8      }
9      ...
10 }
11 kernel void work1(int a){
12     /*do work 1*/
13 }
14 kernel void work2(int a){
15     /*do work 2*/
16 }
```

(2)

Fig. 3. Kernel Fission [12].

5.2 Reducing GPU Memory Access Latency

– **Organizing Data in Global Memory.** Global memory bandwidth allows simultaneous accesses to data elements. However, misaligning data elements in global memory results in serialized accesses, degrading GPU performance through increased memory access latency [23]. In the previous example, using 1024 threads arranged into 64 thread blocks, each containing 16 threads, misaligned 16-data element chunks results in 64 serialized accesses. To combine these 64 accesses into a single transaction, 16-data element chunks need to be contiguous, i.e. aligned to 64 byte boundaries (16 single precision words). Organizing data elements to be aligned in global memory is a crucial optimization as it enables maximum memory bandwidth. It has significantly helped accelerating applications in previous works dealing with data types that have specific alignment requirements, such as structures or arrays [1,28,43].
– **Using Shared Memory.** GPU shared memory has a higher bandwidth than global memory and to efficiently utilize it, the developer does not need to align data elements [42]. Additionally, shared memory offers shorter access time

compared to global memory, as mentioned in Subsect. 3.1. Leveraging shared memory to store frequently accessed data elements, intermediate results, or data elements necessary for inter-thread communication within a thread block can significantly reduce memory access latency [2,43,49]. However, shared memory capacity for each thread block is limited, so careful usage is necessary.

– **Minimizing Shared Memory Bank Conflicts.** Shared memory is split into multiple banks, each accessible by a distinct thread within a thread block. This configuration allows multiple threads to access shared memory simultaneously, as long as they are accessing different banks. In fact, conflicts occur when multiple threads try to access different data elements within the same bank simultaneously, resulting in serialized accesses and increased memory access latency [24]. To reduce bank conflicts, memory padding, a method of transforming data structures without requiring additional source code, can be used [28,39]. This technique resolves bank conflicts by introducing additional empty memory bytes. For example, if an array x[16][16] is shared by threads in a thread block and each thread with thread index "tid" is accessing x[tid][0], it causes a 16-way bank conflict because all threads are accessing different data elements from the same bank. Padding the array in the first dimension with one more element as array x[16][17] completely eliminates bank conflicts. Indeed, now each row has a bank location that is offset by one against the previous row. Although simple and effective, memory padding has the drawback of wasting shared memory.

– **Using Read-only Memory.** Read-only memory, as discussed in Subsect. 3.1, provides faster access compared to global memory. Using read-only memory for data elements that remain unchanged during kernel execution can decrease memory access latency [47,49]. However, this improvement is effective only when threads within the same thread block read the same memory location, otherwise, accesses are serialized [27]. Hence, it is advisable to use read-only memory for reducing memory access latency, but only for constants stored in the same memory locations read by threads within the same thread block.

– **Enhancing Cache Memory Usage.** Nested loops in an application code can provide the developer with the opportunity to apply tiling before GPU offloading, which can improve memory reference locality, enhance multi-level cache memory usage, and reduce memory access latency [18,35,50]. Tiling involves modifying the memory access pattern of the loop to reuse data elements already present in the data cache before they are evicted and need to be reloaded from the global memory. This is accomplished by breaking down the perfectly nested loop into small loops, known as tiles. The tile size being a parameter of this optimization, it is crucial to choose it carefully to fully exploit the tiling of the loops. Indeed, even a small change in sizes has a direct impact on the resulting application acceleration each time [8].

5.3 Discussion

The GPU has unique architectural features that distinguish it from the CPU and requires different programming approaches. Indeed, treating the GPU the same as the CPU ultimately leads to decreased GPU performance, as its specific strengths are not utilized. Hence, understanding GPU's architectural features is crucial in order to fully exploit its capabilities. Table 2 outlines these features and the optimizations for releasing GPU's power, thus accelerating real-time IoT applications.

Real-time IoT application hotspot functions that benefit from GPU offloading for acceleration, vary in nature and can be classified as memory-bound or compute-bound [30]. Memory bound functions primarily engage in memory access, while compute bound ones are predominantly involved in computations. When offloading memory-bound functions, the developer should focus on reducing GPU memory access latency. This can be achieved by aligning data elements in global memory [1,28,43], using shared memory for frequently accessed data elements and intermediate results [2,43,49], minimizing shared memory bank conflicts through padding data elements [28,39], utilizing read-only memory for constants [47,49], and tiling loops to improve cache memory access [18,35,50]. Similarly, when offloading compute bound functions, the focus should be on maximizing GPU parallel execution by organizing threads into multiple thread blocks [17,49], reducing divergent threads through kernel fission [12,21], and enabling concurrent kernels [13,52]. Loop tiling can help make more use of the latter optimization. In this case, parallelism is divided into two levels when GPU offloading : inter-tile parallelism and intra-tile parallelism. Launching the tiles in multiple kernels is used to achieve inter-tile parallelism, and intra-tile parallelism is achieved by processing the inner iterations of each tile on the threads.

To assist the developer identify the nature of hotspot functions and, therefore, the optimizations to focus on, the aforementioned profilers can be utilized. They reveal whether functions spend most of their time accessing memory or the CPU. Most profilers allow for the collection and analysis of execution characteristics on both the CPU and GPU [4,6]. The former aids in determining necessary optimizations, as previously mentioned, while the latter helps fine-tuning these optimizations, such as adjusting the tile size for the desired real-time IoT application acceleration.

Table 2. GPU Performance Optimization to Accelerate Real-Time IoT Applications.

GPU Architectural Feature	Optimization	Memory Bound	Compute Bound
Core Block Parallelism	Thread Block Arrangement		X
SIMT on a Core Block	Kernel Fission		X
Core Blocks for Multiple Kernels	Kernel Concurrency		X
Simultaneous Global Memory Accesses	Data Element Alignment	X	
Shared Memory Short Access Time	Shared Memory Utilization	X	
Simultaneous Shared Memory Accesses	Data Element Padding	X	
Read-only Memory Short Access Time	Read-only Memory Utilization	X	
Cache Memory Short Access Time	Nested Loop Tiling	X	X

6   Conclusion

High-end IoT devices integrate a GPU, which can be programmed to work along-side a CPU in a heterogeneous computing environment. The parallel architecture of the GPU has the potential to accelerate real-time IoT applications based on edge computing. This acceleration can be achieved through a series of steps that have been reviewed in this paper. Initially, hotspot functions within a real-time IoT application must be identified using profilers. Subsequently, the nature of these functions, whether they are memory-bound or compute-bound, needs to be determined, also with the assistance of profilers. The next step involves efficient GPU offloading of hotspot functions by optimizing GPU performance based on their nature. Additionally, fine-tuning the GPU offloading is crucial, also facilitated by profilers that build on the previous step. Through this process, the hidden power of GPUs in IoT devices can be harnessed to accelerate real-time IoT applications and reduce latency.

References

1. Abdelfattah, A., Keyes, D., Ltaief, H.: KBLAS: an optimized library for dense matrix-vector multiplication on GPU accelerators. ACM Trans. Math. Softw. (TOMS) **42**(3), 1–31 (2016)
2. Adámek, K., Dimoudi, S., Giles, M., Armour, W.: GPU fast convolution via the overlap-and-save method in shared memory. ACM Trans. Archit. Code Optim. (TACO) **17**(3), 1–20 (2020)
3. Alqarni, M.A., Mousa, M.H., Hussein, M.K.: Task offloading using GPU-based particle swarm optimization for high-performance vehicular edge computing. J. King Saud Univ. Comput. Inf. Sci. **34**(10), 10356–10364 (2022)
4. AMD: Amd prof (2023). https://amd.com/fr/developer/uprof/uprof-performance-analysis.html. Accessed 20 Dec 2023
5. Amdahl, G.M.: Validity of the single processor approach to achieving large scale computing capabilities. In: Proceedings of the April 18-20, 1967, Spring Joint Computer Conference, pp. 483–485 (1967)
6. ARM: Streamline performance analyzer (2023). https://developer.arm.com/Tools %20and%20Software/Streamline%20Performance%20Analyzer. Accessed 20 Dec 2023
7. Ashouri, A.H., Killian, W., Cavazos, J., Palermo, G., Silvano, C.: A survey on compiler auto tuning using machine learning. ACM Comput. Surv. (CSUR) **51**(5), 1–42 (2018)
8. Baghdadi, R., Merouani, M., Leghettas, M.H., Abdous, K., Arbaoui, T., Benatchba, K., et al.: A deep learning based cost model for automatic code optimization. Proc. Mach. Learn. Syst. **3**, 181–193 (2021)
9. Bridges, R.A., Imam, N., Mintz, T.M.: Understanding GPU power: a survey of profiling, modeling, and simulation methods. ACM Comput. Surv. (CSUR) **49**(3), 1–27 (2016)
10. Cope, B., Cheung, P.Y., Luk, W., Howes, L.: Performance comparison of graphics processors to reconfigurable logic: a case study. IEEE Trans. Comput. **59**(4), 433–448 (2010)

11. CUBIETECH: Allwinner h8 chipset (2023). https://www.cubietech.com/product-detail/allwinner-h8-chipset/. Accessed 10 Dec 2023
12. Daga, M., Scogland, T.R., Feng, W.c.: Architecture-aware optimization on a 1600-core graphics processor. Tech. rep., Department of Computer Science, Virginia Polytechnic Institute & State ... (2011)
13. Dai, H., et al.: Accelerate GPU concurrent kernel execution by mitigating memory pipeline stalls. In: 2018 IEEE International Symposium on High Performance Computer Architecture (HPCA), pp. 208–220. IEEE (2018)
14. Elteir, M.K., Lazem, S., Azab, M.: Unleashing the hidden powers of low-cost IoT boards: GPU-based edutainment case study. J. King Saud Univ. Comput. Inf. Sci. **34**(3), 747–756 (2022)
15. Engel, T.A., Charao, A.S., Kirsch-Pinheiro, M., Steffenel, L.A.: Performance improvement of data mining in WEKA through multi-core and GPU acceleration: opportunities and pitfalls. J. Ambient. Intell. Humaniz. Comput. **6**, 377–390 (2015)
16. Faldu, P., Doshi, N., Patel, R.: Real time adaptive traffic control system: a hybrid approach. In: 2019 IEEE 4th International Conference on Computer and Communication Systems (ICCCS), pp. 697–701. IEEE (2019)
17. Garvey, J.D., Abdelrahman, T.S.: A strategy for automatic performance tuning of stencil computations on GPUS. Sci. Programm. **2018**, 6093054 (2018)
18. Grosser, T., Cohen, A., Holewinski, J., Sadayappan, P., Verdoolaege, S.: Hybrid hexagonal/classical tiling for GPUS. In: Proceedings of Annual IEEE/ACM International Symposium on Code Generation and Optimization, pp. 66–75 (2014)
19. Guide, D.: Cuda c best practices guide. NVIDIA, July (2013)
20. Hamdan, S., Ayyash, M., Almajali, S.: Edge-computing architectures for internet of things applications: a survey. Sensors **20**(22), 6441 (2020)
21. Han, T.D., Abdelrahman, T.S.: Reducing branch divergence in GPU programs. In: Proceedings of the Fourth Workshop on General Purpose Processing on Graphics Processing Units, pp. 1–8 (2011)
22. Hardkernel: Odroid-c4 (2023). https://www.hardkernel.com/shop/odroid-c4. Accessed 10 Dec 2023
23. Hijma, P., Heldens, S., Sclocco, A., Van Werkhoven, B., Bal, H.E.: Optimization techniques for GPU programming. ACM Comput. Surv. **55**(11), 1–81 (2023)
24. Horga, A., Rezine, A., Chattopadhyay, S., Eles, P., Peng, Z.: Symbolic identification of shared memory based bank conflicts for GPUS. J. Syst. Architect. **127**, 102518 (2022)
25. Jazaeri, S.S., Jabbehdari, S., Asghari, P., Haj Seyyed Javadi, H.: Edge computing in SDN-IoT networks: a systematic review of issues, challenges and solutions. Cluster Comput. **24**(4), 3187–3228 (2021). https://doi.org/10.1007/s10586-021-03311-6
26. KADAB: hotspot - a GUI for the Linux perf profiler (2017). https://www.kdab.com/hotspot-gui-linux-perf-profiler/. Accessed 20 Dec 2023
27. Kalaiselvi, T., Sriramakrishnan, P., Somasundaram, K.: Survey of using GPU CUDA programming model in medical image analysis. Inf. Med. Unlocked **9**, 133–144 (2017)
28. Khan, A., Al-Mouhamed, M., Fatayar, A., Almousa, A., Baqais, A., Assayony, M.: Padding free bank conflict resolution for CUDA-based matrix transpose algorithm. In: 15th IEEE/ACIS International Conference on Software Engineering, Artificial Intelligence, Networking and Parallel/Distributed Computing (SNPD), pp. 1–6. IEEE (2014)
29. Khanna, A., Kaur, S.: Internet of things (IoT), applications and challenges: a comprehensive review. Wireless Pers. Commun. **114**, 1687–1762 (2020)

30. Lee, D., Dinov, I., Dong, B., Gutman, B., Yanovsky, I., Toga, A.W.: CUDA optimization strategies for compute-and memory-bound neuroimaging algorithms. Comput. Methods Programs Biomed. **106**(3), 175–187 (2012)
31. Malcolm, J., Yalamanchili, P., McClanahan, C., Venugopalakrishnan, V., Patel, K., Melonakos, J.: ArrayFire: a GPU acceleration platform. In: Modeling and simulation for defense systems and applications VII. vol. 8403, pp. 49–56. SPIE (2012)
32. Munshi, A., Gaster, B., Mattson, T.G., Ginsburg, D.: OpenCL programming guide. Pearson Education (2011)
33. NVIDIA: Jetson Nano developer kit (2023). https://developer.nvidia.com/embedded/jetson-nano-developer-kit. Accessed 10 Dec 2023
34. Ojo, M.O., Giordano, S., Procissi, G., Seitanidis, I.N.: A review of low-end, middle-end, and high-end IoT devices. IEEE Access **6**, 70528–70554 (2018)
35. Park, N., Hong, B., Prasanna, V.K.: Tiling, block data layout, and memory hierarchy performance. IEEE Trans. Parallel Distrib. Syst. **14**(7), 640–654 (2003)
36. Petru, A.M.U.D.B., Peng, E.Z.: General purpose computing on low-power embedded GPUS: Has it come of age? In: 2013 International Conference on Embedded Computer Systems: Architecture, Modeling, and Simulation (SAMOS), pp. 1–10 (2013)
37. Pi, R.: Raspberry pi 5 (2023). https://www.raspberrypi.com/documentation/computers/raspberry-pi-5.html. Accessed 10 Dec 2023
38. PINE64: Pine h64 (2023). https://pine64.com/product/pine-h64-model-b-3gb-single-board-computer/. Accessed 10 Dec 2023
39. Prisacariu, V., Reid, I., et al.: fastHOG-a real-time GPU implementation of hog. Dept. Eng. Sci. **2310**(9), 1–6 (2009)
40. Radxa: Radxa rock (2023). https://wiki.radxa.com/Rock [Accessed: (10 December 2023)]
41. Saadi, H., Nouali Taboudjemat, N., Rahmoun, A., Imbernon, B., Pérez-Sánchez, H., Cecilia, J.M.: Efficient GPU-based parallelization of solvation calculation for the blind docking problem. J. Supercomput. **76**(3), 1980–1998 (2020)
42. Sakdhnagool, P., Sabne, A., Eigenmann, R.: RegDem: Increasing GPU performance via shared memory register spilling. arXiv preprint arXiv:1907.02894 (2019)
43. Sayadi, F.E., Chouchene, M., Bahri, H., Khemiri, R., Atri, M.: CUDA memory optimisation strategies for motion estimation. IET Comput. Digit. Tech. **13**(1), 20–27 (2019)
44. Shete, V., Ukunde, N., et al.: Intelligent embedded video monitoring system for home surveillance. In: 2016 International Conference on Inventive Computation Technologies (ICICT), vol. 1, pp. 1–4. IEEE (2016)
45. Sinha, S.: State of IoT 2023 (2023).https://iot-analytics.com/number-connected-iot-devices. Accessed 7 Dec 2023
46. Stratton, J.A., Anssari, N., Rodrigues, C., Sung, I.J., Obeid, N., Chang, L., Liu, G.D., Hwu, W.: Optimization and architecture effects on GPU computing workload performance. IEEE (2012)
47. Striemer, G.M., Akoglu, A.: Sequence alignment with GPU: prformance and design challenges. In: 2009 IEEE International Symposium on Parallel & Distributed Processing, p. 1–10. IEEE (2009)
48. Stylianopoulos, C., Johansson, L., Olsson, O., Almgren, M.: *CLort*: high throughput and low energy network intrusion detection on IoT devices with embedded GPUs. In: Gruschka, N. (ed.) NordSec 2018. LNCS, vol. 11252, pp. 187–202. Springer, Cham (2018). https://doi.org/10.1007/978-3-030-03638-6_12

49. Stylianopoulos, C., Kindström, S., Almgren, M., Landsiedel, O., Papatriantafilou, M.: Co-evaluation of pattern matching algorithms on IoT devices with embedded GPUs. In: Proceedings of the 35th Annual Computer Security Applications Conference, p. 17–27 (2019)

50. Thambawita, D., Ragel, R.G., Elkaduwe, D.: To use or not to use: CPUs' cache optimization techniques on GPGPUs. In: 2016 IEEE International Conference on Information and Automation for Sustainability (ICIAfS), pp. 1–6. IEEE (2016)

51. Vaidya, A.S., Shayesteh, A., Woo, D.H., Saharoy, R., Azimi, M.: SIMD divergence optimization through intra-warp compaction. In: Proceedings of the 40th Annual International Symposium on Computer Architecture, pp. 368–379 (2013)

52. Wen, Y., O'Boyle, M.F., Fensch, C.: Maxpair: enhance opencl concurrent kernel execution by weighted maximum matching. In: Proceedings of the 11th workshop on general purpose GPUs. pp. 40–49 (2018)

53. Xie, Y., Hu, Y., Chen, Y., Liu, Y., Shou, G.: A video analytics-based intelligent indoor positioning system using edge computing for IoT. In: 2018 International Conference on Cyber-Enabled Distributed Computing and Knowledge Discovery (CyberC), pp. 118–1187. IEEE (2018)

54. Yamato, Y.: Study of parallel processing area extraction and data transfer number reduction for automatic GPU offloading of IoT applications. J. Intell. Inf. Syst. **54**, 567–584 (2020)

Author Index

© IFIP International Federation for Information Processing 2025
Published by Springer Nature Switzerland AG 2025
G. Rey et al. (Eds.): IFIPIoT 2024, IFIP AICT 738, pp. 121–122, 2025.
https://doi.org/10.1007/978-3-031-82065-6

The manufacturer's authorised representative in the EU is Springer
Nature Customer Service Centre GmbH, Europaplatz 3, 69115 Heidelberg,
Germany. If you have any concerns regarding our products, please
contact ProductSafety@springernature.com

Printed and bound by CPI Group (UK) Ltd, Croydon, CR0 4YY
27/04/2026
02097604-0005